THE GRASSES

Pictured Key
Nature Series

How To Know

THE GRASSES

Pictured-Keys for determining the common and
important American grasses with suggestions
and aids for their study.

RICHARD W. POHL

Professor of Botany
Iowa State University

Revised Edition

wcb

WM. C. BROWN COMPANY PUBLISHERS
Dubuque, Iowa

25,157

THE PICTURED-KEY NATURE SERIES

"How to Know the Insects," Jaques, 1947

"Living Things—How to Know Them," Jaques, 1946

"How to Know the Trees," Jaques, 1946

"Plant Families—How to Know Them," Jaques, 1948

"How to Know the Economic Plants," Jaques, 1948, 1958

"How to Know the Spring Flowers," Cuthbert, 1943, 1949

"How to Know the Mosses and Liverworts," Conard, 1944, 1956

"How to Know the Land Birds," Jaques, 1947

"How to Know the Fall Flowers," Cuthbert, 1948

"How to Know the Immature Insects," Chu, 1949

"How to Know the Protozoa," Jahn, 1949

"How to Know the Mammals," Booth, 1949

"How to Know the Beetles," Jaques, 1951

"How to Know the Spiders," Kaston, 1952

"How to Know the Grasses," Pohl, 1953, 1968

"How to Know the Fresh-Water Algae," Prescott, 1954

"How to Know the Western Trees," Baerg, 1955

"How to Know the Seaweeds," Dawson, 1956

"How to Know the Freshwater Fishes," Eddy, 1957, 1969

"How to Know the Weeds," Jaques, 1959

"How to Know the Water Birds," Jaques-Ollivier, 1960

"How to Know the Butterflies," Ehrlich, 1961

"How to Know the Eastern Land Snails," Burch, 1962

"How to Know the Grasshoppers," Helfer, 1963

"How to Know the Cacti," Dawson, 1963

"How to Know the Aquatic Plants," Prescott, 1969

Other Subjects in Preparation

Printed in United States of America

INTRODUCTION

The author has added to this revised edition 25 new genera and 27 additional species of grasses. Three hundred twenty-six species are keyed out and illustrated. The majority of these are the commonest and most important species of American grasses—those that the beginner is most likely to encounter, and those of importance in farming, gardening, weed control, or range and pasture management. Some less common or rare grasses that have unusual interest because of peculiar structures or evolutionary relationships are also included. In addition to those keyed and illustrated, 114 others are mentioned in connection with closely related species, and their distinguishing features are pointed out.

This edition differs greatly from the first in the arrangement of genera into tribes and subfamilies. The changes are so great that I want to explain them to you who have used the first edition. The older version paralleled in arrangement the classic *Grasses of the United States* by Albert Spear Hitchcock and his colleague, Agnes Chase. This work presented an excellent practical classification of the American grasses, and was designed to facilitate the identification of these plants. However, this classification did not make due allowance for the important process of convergent evolution, by which distantly related plants give rise to descendants that resemble each other in superficial characteristics. Some of Hitchcock's published statements indicate that he knew of this hazard, but he was unable to eliminate it from his work since he worked only with characteristics which could be seen with the naked eye or with slight magnification.

The resolution of many of the puzzles of grass relationships began with the work of a Russian, Avdulov, and a Frenchman, Prat. Avdulov, in the early 1930's showed that the grasses could be grouped according to the basic number and size of the chromosomes. However, Avdulov's groupings were not in accord with the then current classifications of grasses and they were largely disregarded. Slightly later, Henri Prat, a French botanist, demonstrated that the leaf epidermis of grasses contained a remarkable variety of specialized cells. The distribution of these peculiar cells also was not in accord with the Hitchcock classification but followed, in a general way, the chromosome number groupings of Avdulov. Prat claimed that some of the groupings of Hitchcock, based mostly on characteristics of the spikelets and the inflorescence, were unsatisfactory and must be abandoned in favor of a system based upon the microscopic characters of the epidermis and chromosomes. Many studies of the last 15 years have confirmed his statements and have suggested the outlines of a new system of classification for the grasses based upon many physical and physiological characters unknown to earlier authors. Some of the features that have been considered in the development of the newer system are the chromosome number and size, the type of specialized cells in the leaf epidermis, the arrangement of tissues in the cross section of the leaf, the nature of the embryo and the seedling, the type of stored food, and others. New observations are frequently reported, and many suggestions as to modifications of the classification of the grasses appear. It is unlikely that an entirely stable arrangement will be reached for some time. However, we can now formulate a system which more accurately reflects the evolutionary relationships of the grasses than was possible when Hitchcock first published the book that was the cornerstone of American agrostology.

One proposed system was published by G. Ledyard Stebbins and Beecher Crampton in 1961. I have used this, with some modifications for which I accept full responsibility, as the skeleton for arranging the subfamilies and tribes of the grasses in this book. Since the system is based largely upon microscopic characters which are not easily observable to most users, it has been necessary to construct new "artificial" keys to the genera of grasses instead of attempting to produce keys to subfamilies or tribes. These keys have been tested by student use. I have also added a brief description of each genus. The naming of genera and species basically follows that of the second edition of Hitchcock's manual, with alterations necessary to bring the usage in accord with recent revisions.

The illustrations have all been made from actual specimens. Drawings marked with the letter B are the work of Mrs. J. Bardach, whose assistance is gratefully acknowledged. Twenty-four of the illustrations have appeared previously in the author's *Grasses of Iowa* and are used here by permission of the Iowa State University Journal of Science. All others are the work of the author.

Ames, Iowa

Richard W. Pohl

The Grass Family is one of the largest of all families of plants in number of species. For a realization of the great importance of grasses to the world, we need think only of corn, wheat and rice. Other grasses provide additional food as well as countless other items that contribute to our happiness and well-being. A study of these interesting plants helps bring understanding of the world and man's place in it.

Dr. Pohl brings to us his wealth of first-hand experience from many years of study and field work with grasses in all of the Continental United States and most of the Canadian provinces. He has made various changes and improvements in this second edition but most important is the new system of classification that is based largely upon evolutionary principles. Anyone with an interest in grasses will find this up-to-date manual a valuable addition to his library.

Mabel Jacques Cuthbert

ISABEL JACQUES CUTHBERT
Editor

CONTENTS

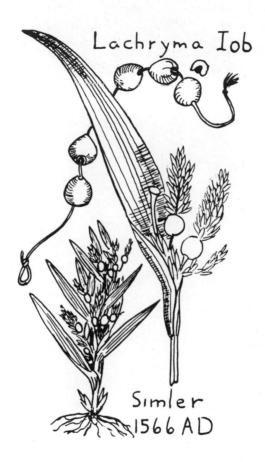

Lachryma Iob

Simler
1566 AD

WHAT IS A GRASS?

F all the world's flowering plants, the grasses are undoubtedly the most important to man. They contribute tremendously to the earth's green mantle of vegetation; they are the source of the principal foods of man and his domestic animals. Without the grasses, agriculture would be virtually impossible: grain, sugar, syrup, spice, paper, perfume, pasture, oil and timber, and a thousand other items of daily use are products of various grasses. They hold the hills, plains and mountains against the destructive erosive forces of wind and water. In the end, they form the sod that covers the sleeping dead.

Despite the fact that the grasses are so important to us, we usually know little about them. Why? Because we think that "All grasses are alike," or "They are too hard to tell apart." But neither statement is true. There are over 5,000 "kinds" or species of grasses in the world and 1,400 of these are found in the United States alone. This book contains descriptions and pictures of over 400 of the more common grasses of our country. While many are superficially similar, they all have good individual marks of recognition. Nobody would at a second glance, for example, confuse foxtail and corn, or quackgrass and oats, or Sudan grass and barley, yet these are all grasses, members of one natural family, the GRAMINEAE, or grass family.

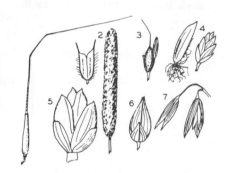

Grasses are easy to recognize. Here are some common ones. 1. Floret of porcupine grass (*Stipa*). 2. Spikelet and panicle of timothy (*Phleum*). 3. Branchlet with spikelets of Johnson grass (*Sorghum*). 4. Floret and spikelet of Kentucky bluegrass (*Poa*). 5. Spikelet of wheat (*Triticum*). 6. Spikelet of proso millet (*Panicum*). 7. Spikelets of oats (*Avena*).

HOW TO RECOGNIZE THE GRASS FAMILY

The grasses and their allies are all members of the great group of flowering plants which we call the MONOCOTYLEDONS. The members of this group are alike in having one seed leaf, parallel-veined leaves (with few exceptions), and stems in which the vascular bundles are scattered in the pith. Among the monocotyledons, members of three families of plants have a "grasslike" appearance and may be confused. These are the grasses (Gramineae), the sedges (Cyperaceae), and the rushes (Juncaceae). A little study of the following key and pictures will show how to separate them quickly and surely.

1

KEY TO GRASSES, SEDGES AND RUSHES

1a Flowers with stiff, greenish or brownish, 6-parted perianth (calyx and corolla); stamens 6 or 3; fruit a many-seeded capsule; leaves usually wiry and round in cross section......................
...................................RUSH FAMILY (JUNCACEAE)

1b Flowers without evident calyx or corolla, gathered into short scaly clusters (spikelets); stamens 3; fruit with a single seed..........2

2a Leaves in 2 vertical rows or ranks; leaf sheaths usually split, with overlapping edges; stems usually round in cross section and hollow between the joints; each flower of the spikelet contained between 2 bracts, the lemma and the palea.....................
..................................GRASS FAMILY (GRAMINEAE)

2b Leaves in 3 vertical rows or ranks; leaf sheaths tubular, not split; stems often triangular in cross section and solid between joints; each flower of the spikelet in the axil of a single bract, the glume
..............................SEDGE FAMILY (CYPERACEAE)

DIFFERENCES AMONG GRASSES, SEDGES, AND RUSHES

GRASS   SEDGE   RUSH

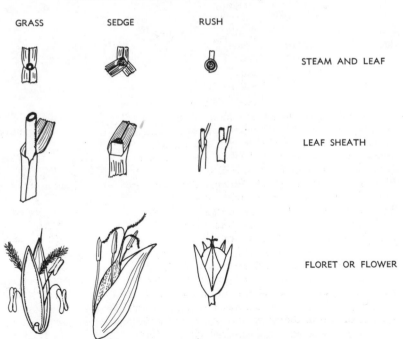

STEAM AND LEAF

LEAF SHEATH

FLORET OR FLOWER

Figure 1

2

WHAT DO GRASSES LOOK LIKE?
ROOTS

The root systems of grasses (Fig. 2) are always fibrous and the majority of the roots arise from the lower nodes of the stems. Because of the fibrous nature of the roots, they are excellent soil binders. When we pull up a grass plant, we remove only a small portion of the total root system, which in many species may reach a depth of six feet or more.

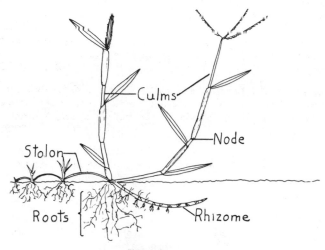

Figure 2

STEMS

The flowering stems or culms of grasses (Fig. 2) are jointed and usually round and hollow between the solid joints (nodes). They may branch, in which case a thin membrane, H-shaped in cross section, lies between the main culm and the branch. It is called a prophyllum (Fig. 3), and it grasps the main culm with two flanges and the branch with the other two. Thus it serves as a brace to the weak V-joint between the main stem and the branch. Stems may be erect, or with bent, knee-like bases (decumbent), or they may trail on the surface of the ground (stolons) and root at the nodes, or they may even grow in the top few inches of soil (rhizomes). The stems of grasses range in size from those like six-weeks fescue, a millimeter or two in diameter and a few centimeters tall, up to the giant bamboos, which may attain a height of a hundred feet and a diameter of a foot or more.

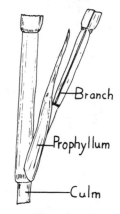

Figure 3

3

LEAVES

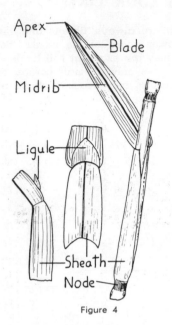

Figure 4

The leaves of grasses are always parallel-veined and generally have long, narrow blades. The foliage leaf of grasses (Fig. 4) consists of a sheath, a ligule, and a blade. There is no petiole. The sheath is the split tubular portion surrounding the culm; the ligule is a little membrane-like or hairy collar which sticks up at the juncture of sheath and blade; the blade is the spreading portion of the leaf. It usually has a conspicuous midrib as well as numerous smaller nerves or veins parallel to the midrib. The tip, or apex, of the leaf is sharp pointed. Little projections at the base of the leaf blade are called auricles. In a few genera, notably *Bromus*, *Melica*, *Schizachne*, and *Glyceria*, the leaf sheath has joined edges, forming a tube, much the same as in the Cyperaceae.

FLOWER CLUSTERS

The flower cluster or inflorescence (Fig. 5) of grasses is always made up of a number of subdivisions called spikelets. The spikelets are arranged in panicles, or 2-rowed spikes, or 1-sided spikes, or

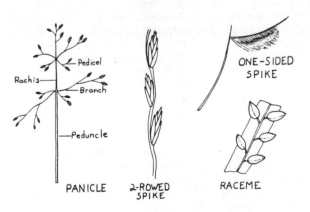

Figure 5

racemes. The parts of the inflorescence include the stalk or peduncle, the central axis or rachis, main and small branches, and the stalks of the individual spikelets or pedicels. At the base of each branch there may be found a little swelling, the pulvinus, which helps spread the branch of the inflorescence when it emerges from the sheath.

SPIKELETS

Since the flowers of grasses are minute, simple, and very similar, they are rarely used in identification. Instead, we look for differences in the bracts (modified leaves) which surround the flowers. The unit subdivisions of the inflorescence are called spikelets (Fig. 6). The simplest sort of spikelet is merely a tiny scaly branchlet of flowers, each flower being surrounded by two bracts. At the base of this branchlet there are two bracts which have no flowers in their axils. These are the first and second glumes. The remainder of the spikelet is made up of flowering units called florets, which are arranged alternately in two rows on a central stalk, called a rachilla, which is usually concealed by the overlapping florets. Each floret consists of an outer bract or lemma and an inner bract or palea, with the naked flower between them. The lemma corresponds to an ordinary foliage leaf, the palea to the prophyllum, and the flower to a branch. During the brief

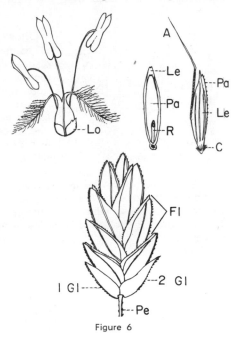

Figure 6

time of flowering, two little blisters, the lodicules, which lie between the ovary of the flower and the lemma, swell up and force the lemma outwards. This allows the stigmas and stamens to protrude. The lodicules are the evolutionary vestiges of a calyx or corolla. If you can find smooth brome grass, orchard grass, or any one of many other grasses in bloom in the morning dew, you can usually observe the lodicules with a hand lens. The actual flower consists of two lodicules, three stamens with long slender filaments, and an ovary with two feathery stigmas. All grasses are wind pollinated except the few which are self pollinated within closed florets (cleistogamous). The lemma has a midrib and a number of smaller "veins" or "nerves" running roughly parallel to it, but converging toward the tip. The midrib of the lemma may be prolonged into a beard or bristle, called an awn. Rarely the lateral nerves also protrude. If the lemma is prominently folded along the midrib, it is said to have a keel. The hardened lower end of the lemma is called a callus. The palea always has two veins near the sides, but lacks a midrib. In some grasses the palea is small or lacking. Usually the spikelet has a stalk or pedicel, or this may be absent, as in wheat and rye, and then the spikelet is said to be sessile. Usually spikelets break up at maturity into individual florets, each of which will then bear a segment of the rachilla. Some spikelets, like those of switch grass and foxtail grass, do not break up, but are shed from the plant whole.

Figure 7

Often it is necessary to determine at what points the spikelets break or disarticulate. When the spikelets are mature and dry, they will disarticulate naturally, but if one has a rather immature plant, it may be necessary to tease the spikelets apart with needles and tweezers or with the finger nail in order to tell where the disarticulation will occur. There are two general types of disarticulation: below the glumes (Fig. 7, a), and above the glumes (Fig. 7, b). Spikelets which disarticulate below the glumes leave nothing on the plant except the stubs of the pedicels. Those which disarticulate above the glumes leave them on the plant. Spikelets of this type usually disarticulate between the florets as well.

Another feature of the spikelet which we may need to know is its shape in cross section. Spikelets may be round in cross section (Fig.

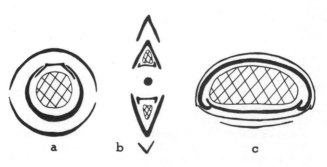

Figure 8

8, a), or flattened from the sides of the glumes and lemmas (laterally compressed), as in Fig. 8, b; or flattened from the backs of the glumes and lemmas (dorsally compressed), as in Fig. 8, c.

The kind of spikelet pictured in Fig. 6 is probably the basic type, from which reduced or more complicated sorts have been derived by various changes. In studying other types of grass spikelets, we should mentally compare them with the basic type in order to decide which parts have been modified or eliminated. The following types of changes are common, and they characterize large groups of grasses:

1. The glumes may become large, covering the whole spikelets (oats and its relatives).

2. The upper florets may become eliminated, so that the spikelet is 1-flowered (red top, timothy, and their relatives).

3. The lower florets may become sterile and much reduced in size, the upper one remaining fertile (canary grass, foxtail).

4. The glumes may become reduced to little ridges on the tip of the pedicel (rice, cut grass).

5. Either stamens or pistil may be eliminated, giving rise to spikelets or plants of one sex (salt grass, creeping love grass, Texas bluegrass, corn, Sorghum, wild rice).

HOW TO COLLECT AND STUDY GRASSES

ROBABLY there is not a county in the United States where less than fifty to one hundred different species of grasses are to be found. Some will be very common and conspicuous, but others will be rare and hard to find. At first, all may look rather similar, so that sharp observation will be needed to detect even all of the common grasses around us. Don't be afraid to get down on hands and knees and crawl to get a good look. Each sort of habitat will have its own grasses: look in prairie, woodland, marsh, bog, ditches, corn or cotton fields, deserts, mountain meadows, or alpine summits, and you will probably be rewarded with a different set of species each time. Even in the same locality, new species come into flower throughout the spring, summer, and fall.

Grasses are easy to collect and prepare, so one should always take care to make good specimens, which will be a pleasure to study later. The tools needed for collecting grasses are simple. First of all, you will need some sort of digger, so that you can get the important underground parts of the plants. I use a long, stout screwdriver, but large hunting knives, geologist's picks, or entrenching tools are also satisfactory. Whatever tools you use, be sure to get the parts of the plant that lie below the ground level. Frequently an otherwise good specimen becomes very difficult to identify because the collector has neglected these structures.

After digging a specimen from the ground, one should knock the soil from the roots or wash them clean. If the plant is too bulky to press flat it may be subdivided and some of the extra inflorescences saved to provide spikelets for dissection. Each specimen is placed in a single folded newspaper sheet (12 x 16 inches as folded) for drying.

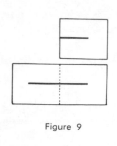

Figure 9

Information which you would like to keep, such as the location, type of habitat, and the date, should be written on the margin of the paper. If the specimen is too long to fit in a folder, it may be doubled back one or more times. Crumpled or tangled parts should be smoothed out. The bent stems can be held in place by little slips of card with a slit cut in each (Fig. 9). The grass specimens in their paper folders may be carried between sheets of beaverboard or plywood, with a light strap around the bundle, for periods as long as a day, before it is necessary to dry them.

Final drying of the specimens is accomplished by placing them, in their folders, between 12 x 18 inch blotters made of builders' deadening felt (obtainable from lumber yards, in rolls), or between thick pads of newspapers. The specimens must be kept under pressure until dry, either by placing boards on the sides of the bundle and strapping it tightly, or by placing heavy weights on top of the bundle. Each day the damp blotters or newspaper pads must be removed and replaced with dry ones. The damp blotters may be dried by laying them out in the sun on dry paving (not grass) for a short while. In wet weather, the blotters can be cautiously dried in a warm oven. Usually grass specimens dry in a few days. After drying, they may be handled in the paper folders, but they will keep better if they are mounted on paper.

One may mount specimens in large scrapbooks, or better still, on standard herbarium sheets which may be purchased from biological supply houses. Specimens may be glued to paper by placing them momentarily on a large sheet of glass covered with thin glue, brushed to a thin uniform layer. Fish glue, carriage glue, or tin paste are satisfactory for this purpose. Each specimen, after gluing, is then dropped onto a sheet of paper. Since grasses are often quite waxy, they do not always stick well and should also be sewed to the sheet with string or fastened down with narrow strips of gummed cloth tape (see Fig. 10). Do not use cellulose tape, since it becomes sticky and brittle with age or pulls loose. A label, bearing the name of the plant, the place and date of collection, and any other pertinent information, should be glued in the lower right corner of the sheet. Loose spikelets or other small parts may be placed in small coin envelopes which are glued to the sheet.

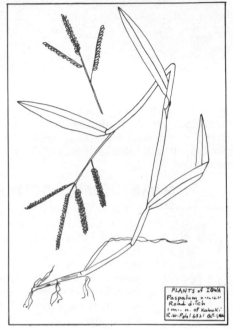

PLANTS of IOWA
Paspalum *******
Road ditch
1 mi. n. of Kabuki
R.W. Pohl 6521 Oct. 1964

Figure 10

When considerable numbers of specimens are needed, for use in classes or for display, they may be preserved by tying them in sheaves and allowing them to hang head down until dry.

The equipment needed to study grasses is simple and mostly very inexpensive. However, thumbs are no substitute for dissecting tools. (Fig. 11) You will need at least two well-sharpened dissecting needles. These should be kept sharp by a fine-grained oilstone, such as a hard Arkansas Case or Behr-Manning stone. A micro-scalpel is needed for cutting small spikelet parts. This instrument can be made from a two-inch piece cut from the end of a jig-saw blade. One end of this, after sharpening, is thrust into a wooden dissecting needle handle. The other end can be shaped with a wire nipper and then sharpened to a cutting edge on the oilstone. Since fingers are

Figure 11

9

bigger than florets, it is essential to have a good pair of tweezers. These should have angle-tips, which must meet perfectly. A razor blade and a metric ruler complete the kit. For those who always lose the ruler, one is printed at the end of this volume.

While it is possible to study grasses with a hand lens, a low power binocular microscope is a great help, since it frees both hands. Relatively low priced ones are now available. If you must use a hand lens, I suggest that you fasten it to an improvised stand.

Dry grass spikelets are often difficult to dissect, as they are stiff and tend to fly away when prodded. A wetting solution can be made from 25% wood alcohol, with the addition of several per cent of strong liquid detergent. Keep this in a dropper bottle and apply as needed. It will also soften leaves so they may be moved without breaking.

SOME USEFUL BOOKS ON GRASSES

 HE following short list includes some of the principal books useful for identification or study of American grasses. The list is not intended to be complete, and some books which are old or unavailable have been omitted. You will find that a book on the grasses of your own state, or an adjacent one, will often make identification easier than such comprehensive works as Hitchcock's manual, which covers a large and diverse area.

Beetle, A. A. 1947. Distribution of the native grasses of California. Hilgardia 17: 309-357. Maps of distributions and discussions of ranges of the species; no keys or descriptions.

Blomquist, H. L. 1948. The grasses of North Carolina. pp. vi plus 276. Keys, descriptions and illustrations. Duke Univ. Press. Durham.

Booth, W. E. 1964. Agrostology. pp. 222. Structure and classification of grasses; no keys or descriptions of individual species. Montana State. Bozeman.

Chase, Agnes. 1959. First book of grasses. Good, well-illustrated explanations of spikelet structure for the various tribes. Smithsonian Institution. Washington, D.C.

Core, E. L., E. E. Berkley, and H. A. Davis. 1944. West Virginia grasses. Bull. 313, West Va. Agric. Expt. Sta. pp. 96. Keys, descriptions, illustrations.

Deam, C. C. 1929. Grasses of Indiana. pp. 356. Keys, descriptions, maps, illustrations. Pub. 82, Indiana Dept. of Conservation. Indianapolis.

Dore, W. G. and A. E. Roland. 1942. The grasses of Nova Scotia. Proc. Nova Scotia Instit. of Sci. XX: 177-288. Keys, discussions, illustrations, maps.

Fassett, N. C. 1951. Grasses of Wisconsin. pp. 173. Keys, maps, illustrations. Univ. of Wisconsin Press. Madison.

Featherly, H. I. 1946. Manual of the grasses of Oklahoma. Bull. 21, Okla. Agric. and Mechan. College. pp. 137. Keys, descriptions, illustrations.

Gates, F. C. 1937. Grasses in Kansas. Rept. of Kansas State Board of Agric., Vol. LV, No. 220-A. pp. 349. Keys, descriptions, illustrations of species, maps.

Gould, F. W. 1965. Grasses of the Texas Coastal Bend. pp. 189. Keys and illustrations.

Harrington, H. D. 1946. Grasses of Colorado. pp. 167, plus index. Keys and descriptions, no illustrations. Mimeographed. Colorado A. and M. College, Fort Collins.

Hitchcock, A. S. 1936. The genera of grasses of the United States, with special reference to the economic species. U. S. Dept. of Agric. Bull. 772, revised ed. pp. 302. Keys to genera, illustrations, discussions of important species. Supt. of Documents. Washington, D. C.

Hitchcock, A. S. 1951. Manual of the grasses of the United States. U.S. Dept. of Agric. Misc. Publ. 200, revised edition (by Agnes Chase). pp. 1051. Abundantly illustrated. This is a very important publication on American grasses, but rather large and complex for the beginner. Supt. of Documents, Washington, D.C.

Hubbard, Wm. A. 1955. The grasses of British Columbia. Handbook 9, B.C. Provincial Museum. pp. 205. Illustrated.

Kucera, Claire L. 1961. The grasses of Missouri. pp. 241. Univ. of Missouri Press. Illustrated.

Mosher, Edna. 1918. The grasses of Illinois. Ill. Agric. Expt. Sta. Bull. 205. pp. 261-425. Keys, descriptions, illustrations.

Norton, J. B. S. 1930. Maryland grasses. Md. Agric. Expt. Sta. Bull. 323. Keys, brief descriptions, key to vegetative characteristics of grasses.

Pohl, Richard W. 1947. A taxonomic study of the grasses of Pennsylvania. American Midland Naturalist 38: 513-604. Keys and habitat notes, no descriptions or illustrations.

Pohl, Richard W. 1966. The grasses of Iowa. Iowa State Journal of Science 40: 341-566. Keys and notes, illustrations, maps.

Pool, Raymond J. 1948. Marching with the grasses. pp. xii plus 210. This is a book on the economic botany of grasses. Not useful for identification of individual genera or species. Univ. of Nebraska Press. Lincoln.

Silveus, W. A. 1933. Texas grasses. pp. xlvi plus 782. Illustrations, keys, and descriptions. Pub. by the author. San Antonio.

U.S. Dept. of Agriculture. 1948. GRASS; The yearbook of agriculture 1948. Contains numerous articles on grasses, legumes, grasslands. One section is on common agricultural grasses. Illustrations. Supt. of Documents. Washington, D.C.

U.S. Forest Service. 1937. Range plant handbook. pp. xxvi plus 512. One section on grasses. Illustrations, detailed notes on structure, uses by grazing animals, range, etc. No keys. Supt. of Documents. Washington, D.C.

11

RECOGNIZING GRASS TRIBES

The basic separation of the grass subfamilies and tribes is made upon microscopic characters, but many of these groups can be recognized by their more obvious features that require little or no magnification. It is helpful to know some of these, and they are summarized below.

Subfamily BAMBUSOIDEAE

All of these grasses have woody perennial stems. The main stems do not have foliage leaves. The leaf blades, which are relatively small, are all found upon small lateral branches. The bamboos seldom bloom. The native and introduced species are all restricted to the southern half of the United States.

Figure 12

Subfamily FESTUCOIDEAE

This group includes many of the common temperate zone grasses. As now defined, it includes far fewer genera than given by Hitchcock. The more readily recognizable tribes are given below.

Tribe FESTUCEAE. Spikelets several-flowered, in panicles; glumes short; lemmas with 5 or more nerves. Bluegrasses, brome grasses, fescues, orchard grass, etc.

Figure 13

12

Tribe TRITICEAE. Spikelets borne on a balanced or sym-metrical spike, 1 or more at each node; florets 1—several; leaf sheaths often bearing auricles. Wheat, rye, barley, quackgrass are examples.

Figure 14

Tribe AVENEAE. Spikelets several-flowered, in panicles; glumes nearly or quite as long as the whole spikelet; awn, when present, from the back of the lemma or from a split tip. Oats, Junegrass.

Figure 15

Tribe AGROSTIDEAE. Spikelets single-flowered, usually quite small, in a pan-icle; compression lateral. See also the tribe Sporoboleae, distinguished only on micro-characters.

Figure 16

13

Figure 17

Tribe STIPEAE. Spikelets single-flowered, round in cross-section; glumes about as long as the body of the lemma; floret hard, cylindrical, with a hard, sharp callus and a stout, usually twisted awn; inflorescence a panicle.

Figure 18

Tribe PHALARIDEAE. Spikelets with long glumes, concealing the florets; florets 2—3, the lower 2 sterile or staminate, often very minute, all falling as a unit from the glumes; inflorescence a panicle.

Subfamily ARUNDINOIDEAE

Tribe ARUNDINEAE. Giant grasses, with stems 1—6 m. tall and large, plumelike panicles, the spikelets covered with silky hairs; florets several; spikelets laterally compressed.

Figure 19

Tribe ARISTIDEAE. This tribe contains only the needle-grasses of the genus *Aristida*. Spikelets single-flowered, the floret hard and cylindrical, with a sharp callus and 3 awns.

Figure 20

14

Subfamily ORYZOIDEAE
Mostly aquatic grasses with single florets and much reduced glumes.

Tribe ORYZEAE. Rice tribe. Spikelets strongly laterally flattened; flower perfect.

Figure 21

Tribe ZIZANIEAE. Wild rice tribe. Aquatic grasses; spikelets tend to be round and are always unisexual.

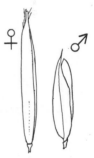

Figure 22

Subfamily ERAGROSTOIDEAE
These grasses were separated from the Festucoideae of Hitchcock on micro-characters. They are largely steppe, desert, and warm climate grasses. Those which resemble Festuceae can usually be recognized by having only 3 or fewer nerves on the lemma.

Tribe SPARTINEAE. This tribe consists of only the genus *Spartina*. Long-lived perennials with an inflorescence of 1-sided spikes, the closely packed, laterally flattened spikelets are single-flowered and disarticulate from the rachis below the glumes.

Figure 23

15

Tribe ERAGROSTEAE. Inflorescence a panicle or a group of 1-sided spikes; spikelets with several to many fertile florets; lemmas 3-nerved.

Figure 24

Tribe SPOROBOLEAE. Inflorescence a panicle; spikelets with a single floret; lemma with 1—3 nerves. Similar to the Agrostideae, but differing in micro-characters.

A

Figure 25

Tribe CHLORIDEAE. Inflorescence of 1—many 1-sided spikes; spikelets with 1 fertile floret and 1 or more rudimentary ones above or below it.

Figure 26

16

Tribe PAPPOPHOREAE. Desert grasses; inflorescence a panicle; lemmas many-nerved, the apex cut into many lobes or many-awned.

Figure 27

Subfamily PANICOIDEAE

Spikelets dorsally compressed, with 1 fertile floret, a sterile or staminate one and a pair of glumes below it.

Tribe PANICEAE. First glume short or lacking; second glume as long as the spikelet; glumes and sterile lemma thin; fertile floret leathery or rigid; inflorescence a panicle or of 1-sided racemes or spikes.

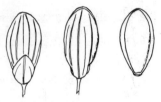

Figure 28

Tribe ANDROPOGONEAE. Both glumes as long as the spikelet and concealing the inner parts; sterile and fertile lemmas thin and delicate; spikelets fundamentally disposed in pairs at each rachis joint; both may be stalked or one may be sessile. The stalked spikelet tends to be reduced or absent. Many variations on the pattern of arrangement occur.

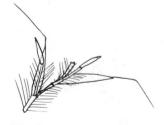

Figure 29

17

GENERAL KEY TO THE GENERA OF AMERICAN GRASSES

1a Stems woody and perennial, several m. tall; main culms bearing
only leafless sheaths which soon fall; leaves with blades only on
smaller branches; plants flowering only at long intervals of years
(Subfamily **BAMBUSOIDEAE**)..........................1. *Arundinaria*

1b Stems not woody, the culms annual; leaves with blades on the main
culm and the branches; plants usually flowering annually......2

2a Spikelets never enclosed in burs,
beads, or bony rachis joints...8

2b Entire spikelets (or at least the
pistillate ones) enclosed in spiny
burs or hard, bony bead-like or
cylindrical structures. Fig. 30....3

Figure 30

3a Spikelets enclosed in spiny burs..............................4

3b Spikelets enclosed in hard or bony structures without hooks or
spines 5

4a Spines of the burs with curved, hooked tips........106. *Tragus*

4b Spines straight and stiff, not hooked.............120. *Cenchrus*

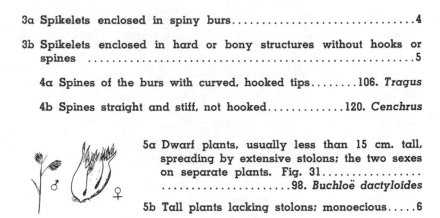

5a Dwarf plants, usually less than 15 cm. tall,
spreading by extensive stolons; the two sexes
on separate plants. Fig. 31.................
.....................98. *Buchloë dactyloides*

5b Tall plants lacking stolons; monoecious.....6

Figure 31

6a Pistillate spikelets borne in hard, bony beads, each bead on a
separate stalk, the staminate spikelets borne on a stalk protruding from an opening at the tip of the bead................
....141. *Coix lacryma-jobi*

6b Pistillate spikelets borne in spikes at the stem tip or concealed
in axillary sheaths, never single..........................7

18

7a Corn-like plants; culms several cm. thick, bearing a terminal tassel of staminate spikelets; pistillate inflorescences hidden in axillary sheaths, made up of a single row of bony joints, each enclosing a pistillate spikelet........................143. *Euchlaena mexicana*

7b Plants not corn-like; culm slender, bearing 1—4 exposed spikes at the tip of each peduncle; basal part of each spike made up of bony cylindrical joints, each enclosing a pistillate spikelet; upper part flattened, each joint bearing 2 staminate spikelets. Fig. 32.............. ....142. *Tripsacum dactyloides*

Figure 32

8a. Tall, thick-stemmed plants with a terminal tassel and axillary cobs covered with husks, the styles (silks) protruding; cultivated crop....................................144. *Zea mays*

8b Plants short or tall, thin or thick-stemmed, lacking separate tassels and cobs...9

9a Fertile floret 1 per spikelet..................................10

9b Florets 2 or more per spikelet..............................102

10a Disarticulation below the spikelets, which fall as a unit or in clusters, attached to rachis joints. Fig. 33A 11

10b Disarticulation above the glumes, which remain on the inflorescence. Fig. 33B 64

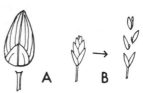

Figure 33

11a Spikelets falling in clusters of 2—many.......................12

11b Spikelets falling singly, usually without attached joints.......28

12a Spikelets surrounded by numerous elongated bristles which fall attached to the spikelets................119. *Pennisetum*

12b Spikelets not surrounded by bristles......................13

19

13a Inflorescence of numerous short, 1-sided spikes which drop as units from a slender unbranched axis. Fig. 34..
...............................97. *Bouteloua curtipendula*

13b Inflorescence not made up of 1-sided spikes...........14

Figure 34

14a Each spikelet group made up of 1 fertile, single-flowered spikelet and several elongated, many-floret sterile spikelets, all on thin pedicels....................16. *Lamarckia aurea*

14b Spikelets not so grouped................................15

15a Inflorescence a much-branched panicle, or of numerous long rames attached to a central trachis................................22

15b Inflorescence a single terminal spike or rame on each peduncle..16

16a Spikelets in trios, the central 1 perfect-flowered and the lateral 2 usually staminate or sterile. Fig. 35....................177

16b Spikelets single, or paired with 1 fertile and sessile and 1 stalked and rudimentary, the pair attached at the base of each rachis joint 17

Figure 35

17a Rachis of the spikes smooth, cylindrical or elliptical in cross-section, the spikelets fitting into hollows of the rachis............18

17b Rachis of the spikes not cylindrical, the spikelets protruding; inflorescence often hairy.....................................19

18a Plants spreading widely by stolons; sheaths flattened and keeled; spikelets sunken in one side of a club-shaped rachis which is elliptical in cross-section.....
....................117. *Stenotaphrum secundatum*

18b Plants not stoloniferous; sheaths not keeled; spikelets sunken into both sides of a cylindrical rachis which disarticulates into individual joints at maturity. Fig. 36
......................................136. *Manisuris*

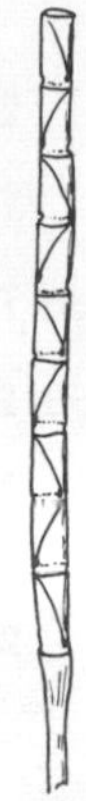

Figure 36

19a Sessile spikelets round, blackish, rough-pitted, 1—2 mm. long, awnless...............................137. *Hackelochloa granularis*

19b Sessile spikelets not round..................................20

20a Spikelets awnless..21

20b Spikelets awned; rachis joints mostly thin and flat........27

21a Spikelets pointed, both spikelets of each pair similar, hairy; erect tall grasses......................................131. *Elyonurus*

21b Spikelets truncate, the apex notched; only the sessile spikelets developed, accompanied by a flattened pedicel bearing a rudiment; low creeping grasses...........................138. *Eremochloa*

22a Each spikelet group (rame) consisting of many consecutive pairs of spikelets, the rames attached directly to the rachis of the inflorescence....................................23

22b Each spikelet group consisting of 1—3 (rarely up to 7) pairs of spikelets, these rames borne in open or dense panicles.....25

23a Sessile spikelet of each pair perfect-flowered, the stalked spikelet reduced in size, awnless, either staminate or rudimentary. Fig. 37........
...................130. *Andropogon*

23b Both spikelets of each pair equal in size and both with perfect flowers
................................24

Figure 37

24a Spikelets awnless 63

24b Spikelets awned............................. 127. *Erianthus*

25a First glume with 2 or 3 awns............. 86. *Lycurus phleoides*

25b First glume not awned....................................... 26

26a Each fertile sessile spikelet accompanied by a stalked staminate one.. 134. *Sorghum*

26b Each fertile sessile spikelet accompanied by a hairy rachis
joint and a hairy pedicel without a spikelet...............
.... 135. *Sorghastrum nutans*

27a Awns hairy, twisted, 5—12 cm. long............ 139. *Heteropogon*

27b Awns not hairy nor twisted, less than 2 cm. long...............
.... 130. *Andropogon scoparius*

28a Glumes absent or so minute as to appear absent; mostly aquatic or marsh grasses.. 29

28b Glumes present, at least the second well-developed........ 32

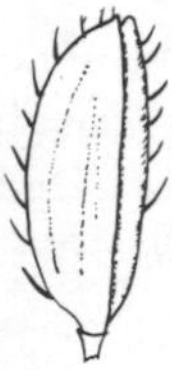

29a Spikelets strongly flattened, perfect-flowered;
plants growing on damp soil or in woods. Fig.
38................................. 69. *Leersia*

29b Spikelets not strongly flattened, unisexual;
plant aquatic............................ 30

Figure 38

30a Plants submerged except for the floating upper leaves; spikelets few, in small clusters.................... 72. *Hydrochloa*

30b Plants tall, emerging from the water; inflorescences large and
many-flowered 31

31a Inflorescence with erect, awned pistillate spikelets at its tip and
drooping, awnless staminate spikelets on the lower branches; annual .... 70. *Zizania*

31b Inflorescence with staminate and pistillate spikelets intermixed on
the same branches; perennial with rhizomes....... 71. *Zizaniopsis*

32a Inflorescence a single spike or raceme on a peduncle..... 33

32b Inflorescence of several to many spikes or a panicle....... 34

33a Axis of spike breaking up into single joints, each bearing an awn-less spikelet; low plants of seacoasts.............60. *Parapholis*

33b Axis of spike remaining intact, the spikelets dropping from it...62

34a Inflorescence of several to many spikes, rames, or racemes..35

34b Inflorescence a panicle, not composed of spikes...........47

35a Spikelets laterally compressed. without sterile florets below the fertile one..36

35b Spikelets dorsally compressed, usually with a sterile lemma below the fertile floret...37

36a Spikelets nearly circular, the glumes equal, concealing the floret. Fig. 39...............
...............26. *Beckmannia syzigachne*

36b Spikelets lanceolate in outline............176

Figure 39

37a Both glumes the full length of the spikelet, firm in texture, enclos-ing and concealing the very thin, delicate sterile and fertile florets
....45

37b First glume usually much shorter than the second, sometimes vesti-gial or absent; glumes thin and membranous in texture, softer than the leathery or rigid floret...................................38

38a Spikelets with a hardened, cup-shaped structure (first glume) protruding at the base. Fig. 40....
...............................111. *Eriochloa*

38b Spikelets lacking a cup-shaped base........39

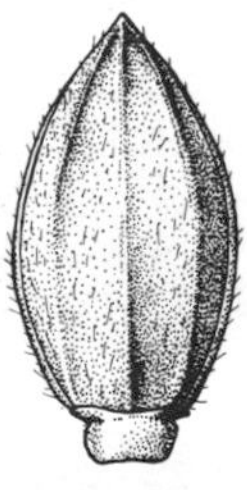

Figure 40

39a First glume absent or less than 1/10 as long as the spikelet...40

39b First glume at least ¼ as long as the spikelet...............43

40a Spikelets concealed by numerous long silky hairs..........
.... 121. *Trichachne*

40b Spikelets smooth or hairy, but not concealed by hairs.....41

41a Fertile lemma hard and stiff, its margins rolled under........42

41b Fertile lemma soft and flexible, its margins not inrolled.........
....122. *Digitaria*

42a Spikelets placed with the back (convex side) of the fertile lemma toward the rachis of the raceme. Fig. 41................109. *Paspalum*

42b Spikelets placed with the back of the fertile lemma turned away from the rachis........
.............................123. *Axonopus*

Figure 41

43a Glumes bearing awns..........................113. *Oplismenus*

43b Glumes without awns......................................44

44a Spikelets placed with the first glume toward the rachis and the back of the fertile lemma away from it..................................110. *Brachiaria*

44b Spikelets placed with the first glume away from the rachis and the fertile lemma toward it. Fig. 41....
....................................108. *Panicum*

45a Low, creeping annuals with broad, cordate leaf blades..........
......................................133. *Arthraxon hispidus*

45b Erect perennials with linear leaf blades; inflorescence silky-hairy
.... 46

46a Inflorescence narrowly cylindrical............126. *Imperata*

46b Inflorescence fan-shaped, of long, spreading racemes........
....128. *Miscanthus*

47a Spikelets densely covered and concealed by long pink or white hairs; Florida.......................125. *Rhynchelytrum repens*

47b Spikelets not concealed by long hairs.......................48

48a Spikelets laterally compressed; no sterile florets below the fertile one 49

48b Spikelets dorsally compressed; a sterile floret or empty lemma usually below the fertile one...........................55

49a Glumes with awns longer than the body.....................
...................................34. *Polypogon monspeliensis*

49b Glumes not long-awned....................................50

    50a "Glumes" much shorter than the floret;
    aquatic plants; cultivated. Fig. 42.......
    ....68. *Oryza sativa*

    50b Glumes as long as the florets........51

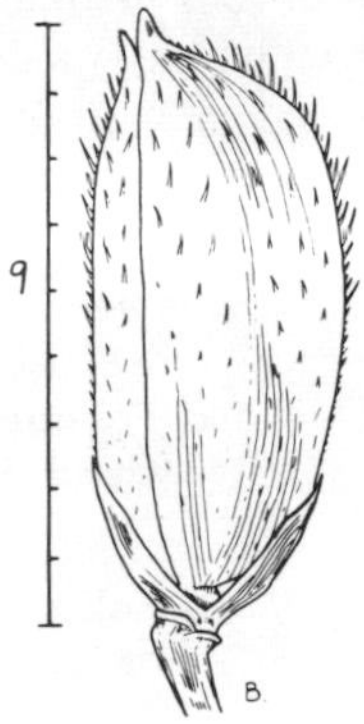

Figure 42

51a Florets 2, the second staminate; plants velvety................
....25. *Holcus lanatus*

51b Floret 1 52

    52a Panicle dense, cylindrical, spikelike; rachilla not
    projecting behind the palea....................53

    52b Panicle open, loose; rachilla prolonged behind the
    palea as a minute bristle. Fig. 43..............54

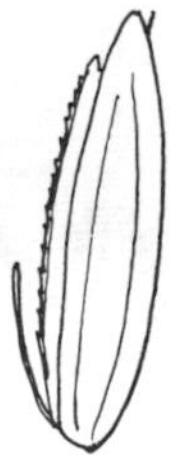

Figure 43

53a Glumes acute, joined together near the base; lemma bearing an
awn...38. *Alopecurus*

53b Glumes truncate, with a projecting midrib, not joined at the base;
lemma awnless....................................39. *Phleum*

    54a Awn of lemma minute or absent...................37. *Cinna*

    54b Awn of lemma twice as long as the spikelet..............
    ....36. *Limnodea arkansana*

55a Inflorescence a dense, spikelike panicle, the spikelets intermixed with numerous bristles which extend beyond them. Fig. 44............118. *Setaria*

55b Inflorescence various, but not spikelike and always
with evident branches; spikelets not interspersed
with bristles...................................56

Figure 44

56a Foliage sticky-hairy; spikelets about 2 mm. long, bearing a
slender awn longer than the spikelet; Florida............
....................................107. *Melinis minutiflora*

56b Foliage not sticky-hairy; spikelets of various sizes, awnless
or awned; not confined to Florida.......................57

57a Second glume or sterile lemma awned (the awn
sometimes reduced to an abrupt point); fertile
lemma pointed. Fig. 45........114. *Echinochloa*

57b Glumes and sterile lemma awnless...........58

Figure 45

58a Second glume sack-like, swollen, the spikelet hence "lop-
sided"; fertile floret about half as long as the sterile lemma
...................................115. *Sacciolepis striata*

58b Second glume not swollen at the base; fertile floret about as
long as the second glume and sterile lemma............59

59a Aerial panicles sterile, the plants producing enlarged underground
spikelets at the tips of slender rhizomes; sandy lands of Atlantic
Coastal Plain................................116. *Amphicarpum*

59b Aerial panicles producing seed; no underground spikelets produced
....60

60a First glume absent or minute, less than 1/10 as long as the spikelet 61

60b First glume present, at least ¼ as long as the spikelet (spikelets with 3 bracts below the fertile floret).......108. *Panicum*

61a Spikelets lanceolate, pointed, on long pedicels in very open, dome-shaped panicles......................124. *Leptoloma cognatum*

61b Spikelets ovoid, blunt, on short pedicels in narrowly cylindrical panicles...................................112. *Anthaenantia*

62a Spikelets with a hairy awn 4—6 cm. long; rhizomes absent.. ....140. *Trachypogon secundus*

62b Spikelets awnless or nearly so, 2—3 mm. long; lawn grasses spreading by extensive wiry stolons and rhizomes........174

63a Giant cultivated plants with thick, solid stems (sugar cane)...... ....129. *Saccharum officinale*

63b Low creeping annual weeds with cordate leaf blades............ ....132. *Microstegium vimineum*

64a Inflorescence a panicle, the spikelets on pedicels........73

64b Inflorescence of one or more spikes, the spikelets sessile...65

65a Inflorescence a single terminal spike, bearing spikelets on both sides of the rachis...........66

65b Inflorescence of one or more 1-sided spikes, the spikelets all on the lower side of the rachis. Fig. 46 67

Figure 46

66a Spikelets 1 per node; delicate small annuals............... ....35. *Scribneria bolanderi*

66b Spikelets 2 per node; awns conspicuous................... ....45. *Elymus caput-medusae*

67a Spikelets with a single floret, no rudimentary ones above it....68

67b Spikelets with 1 or more modified sterile florets above the perfect one 69

68a Plants lacking stolons; rachilla not prolonged beyond the floret; slender spikes arranged singly along a central rachis ....95. *Schedonnardus paniculatus*

68b Plants with extensive creeping stolons; rachilla prolonged beyond the floret as a smooth bristle....96. *Cynodon dactylon*

69a Second glume bearing a protruding bristle at the middle of the keel; inflorescence a single curved spike..93. *Ctenium aromaticum*

69b Second glume without a protruding bristle; spikes 1—many....70

70a Fertile lemma with a single long awn, 3 short awns, or awnless 71

70b Fertile lemma bearing 3 long awns at least twice as long as the body of the lemma..................94. *Trichloris crinita*

71a Spikes borne singly at each node of the rachis................72

71b Spikes borne in 1—several whorls, with 2—many spikes in each whorl...91. *Chloris*

72a Spikes very long and slender (10—20) cm. long), the widely spaced spikelets parallel to the rachis; spikes numerous, forming an open, dome-shaped panicle..........92. *Gymnopogon*

72b Spikes thicker, less than 5 cm. long, the closely packed spikelets placed at an angle to the rachis; spikes 1—many........ ....97. *Bouteloua*

73a Spikelets all unisexual; aquatic grasses......................74

73b Spikelets with perfect flowers.............................76

74a Plants growing immersed in water, the upper leaves 1—5 mm. wide, floating on the water surface...................... ....72. *Hydrochloa caroliniensis*

74b Plants erect, with erect culms, 2—3 m. tall; leaf blades 1—4 cm. wide..75

75a Pistillate spikelets all at the upper tip of the panicle, forming an erect brush, their awns several times as long as the lemma; staminate spikelets all on spreading lower branches of the panicle.. ....70. *Zizania aquatica*

75b Pistillate spikelets short-awned, intermixed with the staminate ones on the same branches and similar to them..................... ....71. *Zizaniopsis miliacea*

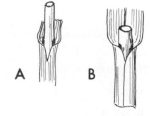

76a Edges of leaf sheaths united. Fig. 47A..........51. *Melica imperfecta*

76b Edges of leaf sheaths overlapping, not united. Fig. 47B...........77

Figure 47

77a Fertile floret dorsally compressed, smooth and shining, awnless
....78

77b Fertile floret not dorsally compressed, either awned or awnless
....79

    78a Panicle densely cylindrical, the spikelets interspersed with numerous bristles; 3 bracts below the fertile floret.........
....118. *Setaria italica*

    78b Panicle open, with naked drooping branches; bristles absent; 2 bracts below the fertile floret.......... 40. *Milium effusum*

79a Floret hard, round in cross section, with faint nerves; awn usually present. Fig. 48.........80

Figure 48

79b Floret soft or leathery, usually more or less flattened and with evident nerves; callus not sharp-pointed. Fig. 49 84

Figure 49

    80a Lemma bearing 3 awns, the lateral 2 often short..........
....67. *Aristida*

    80b Lemma bearing a single awn...........................81

81a Glumes much shorter than the lemma..56. *Brachyelytrum erectum*

81b Glumes as long as the lemma.............................82

    82a Awn bent, twisted at least near the base, firmly attached to the lemma...83

    82b Awn straight or bent (rarely absent), readily separating from the lemma when mature; floret rather short and plump....
....58. *Oryzopsis*

83a Edges of lemma overlapping and concealing the palea; callus usually sharp-pointed. Fig. 48............................57. *Stipa*

83b Edges of lemma turned inward, not meeting, with a deep groove between their edges; callus blunt....59. *Piptochaetium fimbriatum*

84a Glumes minute, less than 1/10 as long as the floret, usually forming a minute cup at the apex of the pedicel..........85

84b Glumes at least ¼ as long as the floret..................87

85a Spikelets with a pair of reduced sterile lemmas, about 1/3 as long as the fertile floret and below it; cultivated aquatic, southern United States..................................68. *Oryza sativa*

85b Spikelet without reduced sterile florets......................86

86a Lemma awned, 3-nerved.........85. *Muhlenbergia schreberi*

86b Lemma awnless, strongly keeled, 5-nerved.......69. *Leersia*

87a Spikelets with 1 or 2 staminate or sterile florets, sometimes reduced to little scales, unlike the perfect floret and below it, falling attached to the perfect floret; both glumes longer than the florets and concealing them. Fig. 50.........................88

Figure 50

87b Spikelets with only a single floret.. 90

88a Lower florets sterile, less than half as long as the fertile one, closely appressed to it; glumes usually wing-keeled, equal.. ....29. *Phalaris*

88b Lower florets as long as the fertile one or longer, glumes not keeled 89

89a Lower 2 florets awned, sterile........27. *Anthoxanthum odoratum*

89b Lower 2 florets awnless, staminate........28. *Hierochloë odorata*

90a One or both glumes longer than the floret (exclusive of the lemma awn, if present)..................................91

90b Glumes shorter than or equalling the lemma...............98

91a Spikelets 10—20 mm. long; coarse, stiff grasses of sand beaches, with long, stiff rhizomes.............30. *Ammophila breviligulata*

91b Spikelets less than 10 mm. long 92

92a Glumes swollen near the base; floret minute, with a slender elongated awn...................33. *Gastridium ventricosum*

92b Glumes not swollen near the base......................93

93a Glumes with extended awn tips 94

93b Glumes lacking awns 95

94a Floret bearing a tuft of hairs at the base; glumes tapering to the awn tip . . . . 85. *Muhlenbergia*

94b Floret glabrous; glumes cut square at the tip, the midrib protruding as an awn . . . . 39. *Phleum pratense*

95a Rachilla prolonged behind the palea as a slender bristle (CARE!); lemma bearing an awn: callus bearing a tuft of straight hairs. Fig. 51 . . 31. *Calamagrostis*

95b Rachilla not extended beyond the floret; callus glabrous or hairy 96

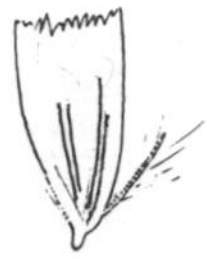

Figure 51

96a Both glumes longer than the floret; lemma glabrous or nearly so . . . . 32. *Agrostis*

96b Second glume longer than the floret, the first shorter 97

97a Floret bearing a tuft of long straight hairs on the callus; plants bearing long rhizomes . . . . 90. *Calamovilfa longifolia*

97b Floret lacking callus hairs; plants tufted . . . . 87. *Sporobolus*

98a Lemma 3-nerved 99

98b Lemma with a single nerve 101

99a Rachilla prolonged beyond the palea; nerves of the blunt lemma parallel, conspicuous, glabrous . . . . 13. *Catabrosa aquatica*

99b Rachilla not prolonged 100

100a Nerves of the lemma silky-hairy nearly to the tip . . . . 89. *Blepharoneuron tricholepis*

100b Nerves of the lemma glabrous, the callus hairy . . . . 85. *Muhlenbergia*

101a Inflorescence short, thick, partially enclosed in the inflated upper leaf sheath . . . . 88. *Heleochloa schoenoides*

101b Inflorescence slender or open . . . . 87. *Sporobolus*

102a Disarticulation below the spikelets, which drop singly or in clusters or remain on the inflorescence 103

102b Disarticulation above the glumes, which remain on the plant. Fig. 52 114

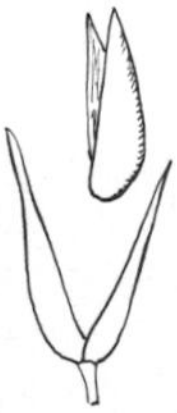

Figure 52

103a Inflorescence a spike, its rachis disarticulating into individual internodes, each bearing one or more spikelets..............104

103b Inflorescence a spike or panicle, the rachis and branches not disarticulating 108

    104a Spikelets 1 at each node of the rachis.................105

    104b Spikelets 2—3 at each node of the rachis.............107

105a Spikes cylindrical, the spikelets fitting into the thickened rachis joints; plants producing good seed.......................106

105b Spikes not cylindrical, the rachis joints thin; plants sterile hybrids.....................................48. *X Agrohordeum*

    106a Spikelets awned.............................44. *Aegilops*

    106b Spikelets awnless; on seacoasts.............60. *Parapholis*

107a Spikelets 3 at each node, each 1 or 2 flowered; sterile hybrids
....49. *X Elyhordeum*

107b Spikelets 2 at each node, each several flowered; plants producing good seed...50. *Sitanion*

    108a Inflorescence a spike.................................109

    108b Inflorescence a panicle...............................111

109a Spikelets not dropping from the spikes; lemmas divided into 5—10 sharp lobes at the tip; California only..............104. *Orcuttia*

109b Spikelets dropping from the rachis when mature; lemmas not lobed at the tip...110

    110a Low tufted annuals; spikelets awnless, dropping singly from the axis; florets 3....................10. *Sclerochloa dura*

    110b Stoloniferous or rhizomatous perennials; spikelets awned, dropping in groups of 3, each with 1 or 2 florets..........
    ....100. *Hilaria*

111a Spikelets dropping in clusters of 2—4 each, including a single-flowered fertile and several multiple-flowered sterile spikelets..
..................................16. *Lamarckia aurea*

111b Spikelets dropping singly..............................112

    112a Florets 2, sheaths with overlapping edges..............113

    112b Florets 3 or more, the upper ones sterile and rolled into a club-shaped rudimentary structure; sheaths with united edges
    ....51. *Melica*

113a Second floret awned, staminate; glumes pubescent; plants velvety-hairy to the touch......
.........................25. *Holcus lanatus*

113b Florets awnless, perfect-flowered; glumes not pubescent, the second much wider than the first; plants not velvety to the touch. Fig. 53
.........................23. *Sphenopholis*

Figure 53

32

114a Inflorescence an open or dense panicle or a raceme, the spikelets on pedicels....126

114b Inflorescence of balanced or 1-sided spikes....115

115a Spike balanced, the spikelets on both sides of the rachis; only 1 spike per culm....121

115b Spikes 1-sided, the spikelets all on the lower side of the rachis; spikes several to many at the tip of each culm or branch....116

116a Low annual, forming mound-shaped clumps; leaf blades short, bristly-pointed; spikelets mostly concealed within the upper leaf sheaths; florets 2—4.....99. *Munroa squarrosa*

116b Annuals or perennials; foliage not bristly; spikelets not concealed within the leaf sheaths; florets 1 or more....117

117a Flowers staminate; low stolon-bearing plants, usually less than 10 cm. tall; Great Plains....98. *Buchloë dactyloides*

117b Flowers perfect; plants of various aspects....118

118a Spikelets with a single perfect floret, 1 or more sterile rudimentary, usually awned ones above it....91. *Chloris*

118b Spikelets with several perfect florets....119

119a Spikes numerous, forming a panicle....76. *Leptochloa*

119b Spikes few, usually less than 6, all arising from the apex of the culm....120

120a Rachis of each spike extending beyond the spikelets as a naked point; second glume awned....78. *Dactyloctenium aegyptium*

120b Rachis of each spike covered with spikelets to the tip; glumes without awns....77. *Eleusine indica*

121a Spikelets 1 at each node of the rachis....122

121b Spikelets 2 or more at each node of the rachis....125

122a Spikelets placed edgewise to the rachis; only the glume on the side away from the rachis present. Fig. 54....5. *Lolium*

122b Spikelets placed flatwise against the rachis; both glumes present....123

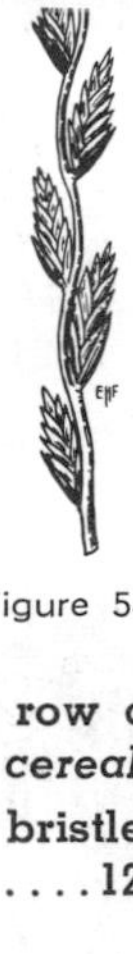

Figure 54

123a Spikelets with only 2 florets; keels of lemmas bearing a row of short, stiff bristles; cultivated annual grain...43. *Secale cereale*

123b Spikelets with 3 or more florets; keels of lemmas without bristles....124

124a Glumes lanceolate, acute, more than twice as long as wide; grain remaining enclosed by the lemma and palea; plants perennial....................................41. *Agropyron*

124b Glumes broadly ovate, blunt, less than twice as long as wide; grain falling free of the lemma and palea; cultivated annuals.............................42. *Triticum aestivum*

125a Glumes very short or lacking; spikelets spreading at right angles to the rachis............................46. *Hystrix patula*

125b Glumes nearly as long as the lowermost floret; spikelets erect, pressed against the rachis...........................45. *Elymus*

126a Giant grasses, the culms 2—6 m. tall and often very thick; panicles large, plumelike, with the spikelet covered with silky hairs attached to the rachilla or lemmas..........127

126b Grasses of lower stature, usually less than 1.5 m. tall; spikelets not covered with silky hairs................129

127a Lemmas hairy..128

127b Lemmas glabrous, the rachilla joints densely silky; plants of wet ground and marshes.................62. *Phragmites communis*

128a Leaves mostly basal, long and narrow, drooping; plants forming large clumps of leaves.....63. *Cortaderia selloana*

128b Leaves equally spaced along the culms, broad and with clasping blade bases..................61. *Arundo donax*

129a Glumes at least 2/3 as long as the entire spikelet, excluding the awns 130

129b Glumes much shorter than the spikelet, usually not reaching above the tip of the lowermost floret......................145

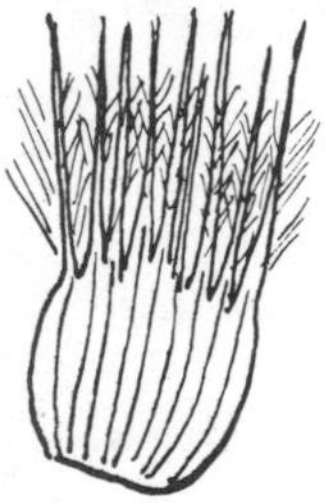

Figure 55

130a Lemma with 9 or more awns. Fig. 55..131

130b Lemma awnless or with 1—3 awns....132

131a Florets 3; awns fringed with hairs....103. *Enneapogon desvauxii*

131b Florets 4 or more; awns not hairy............102. *Pappophorum*

132a All florets falling together as a unit from the glumes..133

132b Florets disarticulating from each other and falling separately 136

133a Florets 4, awned, the uppermost one reduced to an awned rudiment; low annual of southwestern deserts.....................
....82. *Blepharidachne kingii*

133b Florets 2—3, the uppermost one fertile.....................134

134a Lower 2 florets less than half as long as the fertile floret and appressed to it; glumes keeled and winged. Fig. 56.....................29. *Phalaris*

134b Lower 2 florets as long as the fertile one or longer.................135

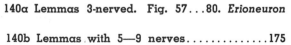

Figure 56

135a Lower florets awned, sterile........27. *Anthoxanthum odoratum*

135b Lower florets awnless, staminate..........28. *Hierochloë odorata*

136a Paleas never long-hairy; spikelets over 1 cm. long.....137

136b Paleas either glabrous or long-hairy; spikelets usually less than 1 cm. long......................................139

137a Awn attached on the back of the lemma....................138

137b Awn attached between 2 teeth at the tip of the lemma.........
....64. *Danthonia*

138a Spikelets drooping; glumes 7—9 nerved, over 2 cm. long; annuals..17. *Avena*

138b Spikelets erect; glumes 3—5 nerved, less than 2 cm. long; perennials...............................18. *Helictotrichon*

139a Spikelets with 3 or more florets..........................140

139b Spikelets with only 2 florets.............................141

140a Lemmas 3-nerved. Fig. 57...80. *Erioneuron*

140b Lemmas with 5—9 nerves..............175

Figure 57

141a Lower floret staminate, with a bent, twisted awn; upper floret perfect, with a short, straight awn.....19. *Arrhenatherum elatius*

141b Both florets alike and perfect.............................142

142a Florets awnless; rachilla joint very short, not long-hairy...
..................................24. *Koeleria cristata*

142b Florets usually awned; rachilla joints often long-hairy..143

143a Awn attached near the base of the lemma.................144

143b Awn attached above the middle of the lemma or absent.......
....22. *Trisetum*

144a Rachilla prolonged beyond the base of the upper floret as a minute hairy bristle...................20. *Deschampsia*

144b Rachilla not prolonged beyond the second floret..21. *Aira*

145a Lemma with 3 or more long awns.........................146

145b Lemma not possessing 3 or more long awns...............147

146a Each floret with 3 awns; all the florets falling together as a cigar-shaped unit with many awns; plants monoecious or dioecious; stolons present.......84. *Scleropogon brevifolius*

146b Each floret with 9 or more awns, disarticulating separately; spikelets perfect-flowered.......101. *Cottea pappophoroides*

147a Lemmas with 1—3 conspicuous nerves....................148

147b Lemmas with 5 or more nerves, which are usually inconspicuous
....157

148a Lemmas 1-nerved; spikelets paired, one fertile, with 2 or 3 flowers, the other sterile and with many florets; inflorescence a dense, spikelike panicle..........15. *Cynosurus cristatus*

148b Lemmas 3-nerved; spikelets all alike, not paired; inflorescence an open or spikelike panicle...................149

149a Spikelets not disarticulating; florets all staminate; stoloniferous plants of dry plains and deserts......84. *Scleropogon brevifolius*

149b Spikelets disarticulating above the glumes and between the florets, or the lemmas dropping from the persistent rachilla; flowers perfect 150

150a Inflorescence a small, dense tuft of a few spikelets, partially surrounded by leaves; small stoloniferous plants of southwestern plains and deserts.................80. *Erioneuron*

150b Inflorescence an open or dense panicle which is supported above the leaves on a peduncle......................151

151a Nerves or callus of the lemmas hairy.....................152

151b Nerves and callus not hairy.............................154

152a Nerves of lemma glabrous, the callus with a tuft of conspicuous straight hairs; sand grasses of the Great Plains; rhizomes slender, elongated..................83. *Redfieldia flexuosa*

152b Nerves of the lemma conspicuously pubescent; plants lacking rhizomes...153

153a Palea fringed with long hairs on its upper half; plants shallow-rooted annuals.......................,,..... .81. *Triplasis purpurea*

153b Palea not fringed with long hairs on its upper half; perennials...
....79. *Tridens*

154a Lemmas notched or split at the tip. Fig. 58.....
........................79. *Tridens albescens*

154b Lemmas not notched or split at the tip......155

Figure 58

155a Grain large, bottle-shaped, 5—6 mm. long, forcing the stiff, strongly-keeled lemma and the palea apart at maturity and protruding between them. Fig. 59.........55. *Diarrhena americana*

155b Grain not bottle-shaped nor forcing the floret open and not over 2 mm. long; lemmas thin..
....156

Figure 59

156a Spikelets with 3 or more florets; lemmas pointed, the nerves converging; plants of dry or moist soil.......75. *Eragrostis*

156b Spikelets with 2 florets; lemmas with blunt tips and parallel nerves; aquatic grasses, mostly in the northern Rocky Mountains...............................13. *Catabrosa aquatica*

157a Plants dioecious, the spikelets of the two sexes similar........158

157b Plants perfect-flowered 160

158a Lemmas with numerous faint nerves; plants of salty or alkaline soil.....................................73. *Distichlis*

158b Lemmas 5-nerved; plants ordinarily not on salty soil....159

159a Plants clump-forming, rarely with rhizomes; lemmas glabrous; Rocky Mountains..........................4. *Leucopoa kingii*

159b Plants turf-forming by rhizomes; lemmas hairy on the keel or callus; Pacific coastal sand dunes or south central and southeastern states..11. *Poa*

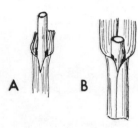

Figure 60

160a Edges of sheaths united, not overlapping (except when torn by expansion of the stem). Fig. 60A..
............................161

160b Edges of sheaths separate, overlapping. Fig. 60B............166

161a Spikelets densely bunched near the tips of the few, stiff panicle branches, almost sessile; sheaths keeled...14. *Dactylis glomerata*

161b Spikelets not bunched, all on pedicels; sheaths not keeled....162

162a Inflorescence a raceme of a few large awned spikelets; Pacific Coast States.......................54. *Pleuropogon*

162b Inflorescence a panicle; spikelets awned or awnless....163

Figure 61

163a Lemmas awnless, blunt, with prominent parallel nerves; spikelets shattering very readily; plants of wet soil or shallow water. Fig. 61.......53. *Glyceria*

163b Lemmas acute, awned, or with split tips; nerves of the lemmas converging toward the tips.............164

164a Florets bearing a conspicuous tuft of straight erect hairs on the callus; lemmas awned.....52. *Schizachne purpurascens*

164b Florets without tufts of callus hairs; lemmas awned or awnless 165

38

165a Upper several florets of the spikelet sterile, wrapped around each other, forming a club-shaped rudimentary structure. Fig. 62..........................51. *Melica*

165b Upper florets not sterile, not wrapped around each other....................................2. *Bromus*

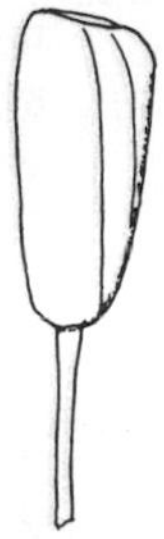

Figure 62

166a Spikelets very flat, the lemmas strongly keeled, with many faint nerves; one or more of the lower florets empty......
....66. *Uniola*
166b Spikelets not strongly flattened; lower florets fertile.....167

167a Lemmas nearly circular in outline, awnless, oriented at right angles to the rachilla...................................12. *Briza*

167b Lemmas longer than wide, appressed to the rachilla at an acute angle 168

168a Lemmas bearing a tuft of cottony hairs attached to the callus. Fig. 63....................11. *Poa*

168b Lemmas without cottony hairs on the callus..169

Figure 63

169a Lemmas bearing awns...............................3. *Festuca*

169b Lemmas without awns....................................170

170a Lemmas with blunt tips; nerves faint or conspicuous, running parallel to the tip..............................173

170b Lemmas tapering to an acute tip or awn-tipped; nerves usually inconspicuous, usually converging toward the tip of the lemma 171

171a Low annuals with small panicles, less than 10 cm. long, their branches rigid and nearly simple; rachis and branches triangular; pedicels shorter than the 5—10 flowered spikelets and thick, rigid, and triangular in cross section...............9. *Scleropoa rigida*

171b Annuals or perennials of various sizes; panicles small or large; rachis and branches usually round; pedicels thin and flexible, usually longer than the spikelets..........................172

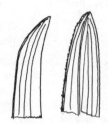

172a Lemmas sharp-pointed or awn-tipped; leaf blades tapering to fine points......
............................3. *Festuca*

172b Lemmas not sharp-pointed; leaf blades with blunt, boat-shaped tips. Fig. 64..
...............................11. *Poa*

Figure 64

173a Nerves faint; lemmas usually with golden or purplish transverse bands below tip; plants usually on salty or alkaline soil........
....6. *Puccinellia*

173b Nerves conspicuous; lemmas green or with a purple band below the tip; plants of wet ground or water.......7. *Torreyochloa*

174a Spikelets laterally compressed, stalked, acute
...............................105. *Zoisia*

174b Spikelets dorsally compressed, not stalked; first glume truncate and notched at the center. Fig. 65...........................138. *Eremochloa*

Figure 65

175a Miniature tufted desert annuals; southwestern United States; lemmas blunt, split at the tip, 7—9 nerved...........65. *Schismus*

175b Tall rhizomatous marsh grass, north central United States; lemmas acute...........................8. *Scolochloa festucacea*

176a Leaf blades broad, cordate-based; creeping annual........
.................................133. *Arthraxon hispidus*

176b Leaf blades linear; erect rhizomatous perennials...........
....74. *Spartina*

177a Spike disarticulating at the base of each joint, the spikelet group
falling attached to the internode...................47. *Hordeum*

177b Spike not disarticulating, the rachis remaining intact when mature 178

178a All 3 spikelets producing grains; annual crop plant; leaves
with strong auricles........................47. *Hordeum*

178b Only the central spikelet producing a grain, the lateral 2
staminate; rhizomatous or stoloniferous perennials; leaves
without auricles..............................100. *Hilaria*

PICTURED-KEYS TO COMMON AMERICAN GRASSES

SUBFAMILY I. BAMBUSOIDEAE BAMBOO SUBFAMILY

Tribe 1. Arundinarieae

1. ARUNDINARIA   CANE

CANE

Arundinaria gigantea (Walt.) Chapm.

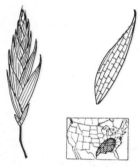

Figure 66

Stems (canes) woody, perennial, reaching as much as 10 m. in height; plants rarely flowering. Cane grows in dense colonies, called canebrakes, in river bottomlands from Virginia to the Ohio Valley and southward to eastern Texas and Florida. The canes are used for fish poles, basketry, and in a variety of other ways. The young shoots and leaves are eagerly taken by domestic animals. A smaller form of cane, with culms usually less than 2 m. tall, is called *Arundinaria tecta* Walt. Muhl.

This species can be distinguished by the presence of air canals in the rhizomes. These are lacking in *A. gigantea*.

While cane is our only native bamboo, a number of other species are sometimes grown for ornament. Hardiest of these is *Pseudosasa japonica*, a small bushy bamboo reaching 2—3 m. tall, spreading by rhizomes and forming dense colonies.

SUBFAMILY II. FESTUCOIDEAE
FESTUCOID SUBFAMILY

Tribe 2. Festuceae

2. BROMUS   BROME GRASSES

1a Spikelets strongly laterally flattened, 2—4 cm. long; lemmas V-shaped in cross section.......................................2

1b Spikelets not strongly flattened, round in cross section before flowering; lemmas rounded on the back...........................3

2a Lemmas awnless or with a short awn less than 2 mm. long. Fig. 67.

    RESCUE GRASS   *Bromus unioloides* H.B.K.

Annual; tufted; culms up to 100 cm. long, erect or spreading; leaf sheaths and blades glabrous or hairy, dark green; panicles open, up to 20 cm. long; spikelets 2—3 cm. long, with 6—12 florets; lemmas glabrous or rarely hairy, about 1.5 cm. long, much flattened and closely overlapping. Rescue grass got its name from its winter annual habit, which makes it one of the earliest forage grasses in the South. It is planted in the fall for winter and spring pasture, but in many areas it has escaped from cultivation and is regarded as a wild plant. With good moisture, it makes lush, highly palatable forage. Heavy rich soil, bottomlands. Native to South America. March—June.

Figure 67

2b Lemmas bearing awns 5—15 mm. long. Fig. 68.
MOUNTAIN BROME   *Bromus carinatus* **H. & A.**

Annual or biennial; tufted; plants 50—100 cm. tall or taller, vigorous and leafy; panicles 15—30 cm. long, with spreading or drooping branches; sheaths and leaf blades smooth or hairy; blades ranging from narrow and involute to broad and flat. A number of closely related and intergrading plants, sometimes recognized as separate species, are included here. These plants are common on open ground and in thin woods in the western states and furnish a good deal of range forage. The foliage and the seed heads are eaten, the latter furnishing a good fattening ration for lambs. The seed of these plants is now available in commerce and the plants are used for range re-vegetation in the West. March—June.

Figure 68

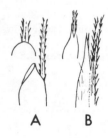

3a Lemmas broad, rounded or tapered to the apex, the lateral teeth at the base of the awn blunt or united. Fig. 69A...................4

3b Lemmas narrow, with a hard sharp callus and long, sharp lateral teeth at the base of the awn. Fig. 69B...........................16

A   B

Figure 69

4a First glume 1-nerved, narrowly lanceolate......................5

4b First glume 3—5-nerved, ovate or elliptical.....................9

5a Plants tufted, without rhizomes; panicles mostly drooping; lemmas bearing well developed awns...................................6

5b Plants bearing rhizomes; panicles erect, with ascending branches; lemmas awnless or with very short awns, 1—2 mm. long. Fig. 70.
SMOOTH BROME *Bromus inermis* **Leyss.**

Perennial; 50—100 cm. tall; panicles 10—20 cm. long. Smooth brome, introduced from Eurasia, is one of our most successful forage grasses, and has been very widely planted in the United States for pasture and hay production. It frequently escapes to roadsides, ditches, and moist wooded areas. June—August.

Bromus pumpellianus Scribn. is a closely related species, native to the western states from the Black Hills to Colorado and Alaska. It has rhizomes but the lemmas are hairy. It hybridizes with *B. inermis*.

Figure 70

6a Lemmas pubescent along the margins and lower part of the back, the central portion glabrous. Fig. 71..........7

Figure 71

6b Lemmas pubescent across the back............................8
7a Ligule 3—5 mm. long; awns 5 mm. or more long; plants of the western states. Fig. 72.

Bromus vulgaris **(Hook.) Shear**

Perennial; tufted; plants slender; culms 80—120 cm. tall; ligules prominent; leaf blades up to 12 mm. wide; panicles drooping, 10—15 cm. long; spikelets about 2.5 cm. long; lemmas usually 8—10 mm. long, hairy on the margins, glabrous or nearly so on the back; awns 5—8 mm. long. Moist rocky woods and canyons. Forms with nearly glabrous foliage and lemmas are known. July—August.

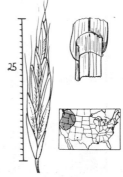

Figure 72

7b Ligule about 1 mm. long; awn 3—5 mm. long; plants widespread. Fig. 73.

Bromus ciliatus L.

Perennial; tufted; plants 70—120 cm. tall; panicles 15—25 cm. long, drooping. Leaf sheaths glabrous or somewhat hairy; blades smooth or hairy, up to 1 cm. wide. This species has handsome fringed spikelets. It is one of the most widespread of the native woodland bromes in moist rocky or alluvial woods. It provides excellent forage in the western states. July—August.

Figure 73

8a Culms with 3—7 nodes; sheaths without auricles. Fig. 74.

Bromus pubescens L.

Perennial; tufted, in small clumps; culms erect or leaning; plants usually 60—150 cm. tall; panicles open, drooping, usually 15—20 cm. long; leaf sheaths shorter than the internodes, hairy or rarely glabrous; leaf blades 5—17 mm. wide; lemmas rather uniformly hairy across the back. This is the commonest woodland brome in the eastern United States. It is to be found in nearly every moist woods. Called B. purgans in recent manuals. June—July.

Forma glabriflorus is a form of this species which has glabrous lemmas. It may be distinguished from other similar woodland bromes by the anthers, which are 3—4.5 mm. long.

Figure 74

8b Culms with 10—20 nodes, the sheaths longer than the internodes, bearing pointed appendages (auricles) at the throat. Fig. 75.

Bromus purgans L.

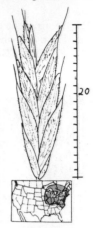

Perennial; tufted; culms up to 2 m. tall; panicles usually 15—25 cm. long, rather dense. Leaf sheaths longer than the internodes, hence overlapping. This species blooms several weeks later than *B. pubescens*. These two species frequently grow together. The sheaths are often covered with dense grayish wool. Alluvial bottomlands; prairies. Called *B. latiglumis* in most manuals. July—September.

Figure 75

9a Panicle open, pyramid-shaped, erect or drooping 10

9b Panicle dense, ovoid, erect, with short branches and overlapping spikelets 15

10a Lemmas glabrous or scabrous 11

10b Lemmas heavily pubescent 14

11a Lemmas bearing awns, not broad or inflated 12

11b Lemmas awnless or with minute awn tips, very broad and inflated. Fig. 76.

RATTLESNAKE CHESS   *Bromus brizaeformis* F. & M.

Annual; tufted; plants 30—60 cm. tall; panicles drooping, 5—15 cm. long. The odd, inflated spikelets of this species look much like the rattlers of a rattlesnake. It is sometimes planted for ornament and is occasionally found naturalized in fields and waste ground in the western states and elsewhere. Introduced from Europe. June—August.

Figure 76

12a Lemmas overlapping; rachilla not exposed; awns well developed; upper sheaths pubescent.....................................13

12b Margins of lemmas rolling inward at maturity, exposing the rachilla; awns short, kinked; upper sheaths glabrous. Fig. 77.
    CHESS, CHEAT   *Bromus secalinus* L.

Annual; tufted; plants 30—60 cm. tall; panicles 7—12 cm. long. Chess is a common weed of roadsides and grainfields. The quickly maturing seeds may be harvested with wheat or other small grains and re-planted elsewhere. It is particularly common where wheat is grown. Introduced from Europe. Old super-stition claimed that cheat came from degenerate small grains, hence the name. May—July.

Figure 77

13a Mature spikelets 3—5 mm. wide; lower sheaths densely woolly with tangled or matted soft hairs. Fig. 78.
    JAPANESE BROME   *Bromus japonicus* Thunb.

Annual; tufted; plants 40—70 cm. tall; panicles drooping, with delicate, flexuous branches. The awns may be straight or bent, depending upon their moisture content. Japanese brome was introduced from the Old World, and is now a very widespread weed of roadsides, fields, and waste ground. May—August.

Bromus arvensis L., FIELD BROME, is similar to this species but has more slender spikelets and an-thers 3—4 mm. long, those of *B. japonicus* being under 2 mm. long. Field brome is rare in this coun-try, but has been promoted by a few seedsmen in recent years.

Figure 78

13b Mature spikelets 5—8 mm. wide; lower sheaths covered with straight spreading stiff hairs. Fig. 79.

Bromus commutatus Schrad.

Annual; tufted; plants usually 30—100 cm. tall, freely branching from the base; foliage hairy; panicles open, pyramidal, usually 5— 15 cm. long. In plants growing on sterile dry soil, the inflorescence may be reduced to a raceme of a few spikelets. Such plants closely resemble *B. racemosus* (see Fig. 83). This species is closely related to *B. secalinus*, from which it differs in the greater hairiness of the foliage and more overlapping florets. Along with *B. japonicus* and *B. secalinus*, this species is a widespread weed of fields and waste places. It is particularly common in the eastern and far western states, but apparently somewhat rare in the Middle West. Introduced from Europe. June—July.

Figure 79

14a Leaf blades 2—4 mm. wide, sparsely hairy; from North Dakota to western Texas and westward. Fig. 80.

Bromus anomalus Rupr.

Perennial; tufted; culms slender, 30—60 cm. tall; nodes hairy; sheaths somewhat hairy or glabrous; panicles small, drooping, usually 10 cm. long or shorter; spikelets few, drooping, densely hairy; first glume with 3 nerves, the second with 5; lemmas about 12 mm. long, the awns 2—4 mm. long. *Bromus anomalus* is widespread and common in the Rocky Mountain region, where it is regarded as a very valuable forage grass for all kinds of domestic livestock and for wild grazing animals. It grows in aspen, spruce, and pine forests and on open ground in meadows and parks, at elevations up to 3000 m. July—September.

Var. *lanitipes* (Shear) Hitch. has woolly sheaths.

Figure 80

14b Leaf blades 5—10 mm. wide, densely hairy; Minnesota and Iowa eastward. Fig. 81.
WILD CHESS *Bromus kalmii* A. Gray

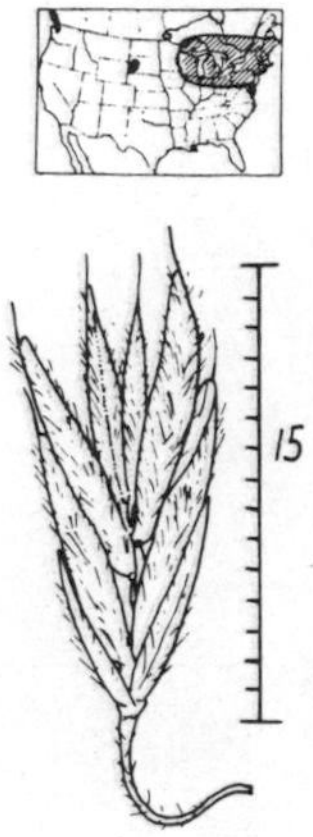

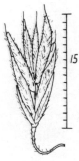

Perennial; tufted; plants 50—100 cm. tall; panicles small, 5—10 cm. long, drooping. The lemmas are very conspicuously hairy. This and the preceding species are the only native perennial woodland species with 3-nerved first glumes. Roadsides and open woods. July—August.

Figure 81

15a Lemmas hairy. Fig. 82.

Bromus mollis L.

Annual; tufted; plants 20—80 cm. tall; leaf sheaths and blades softly hairy; panicles stiff, dense, and erect, 5—10 cm. long; glumes and lemmas hairy; first glume with 3 or 5 nerves, the second with 5 or 7; lemmas soft, with 7 nerves, usually 7—9 mm. long. This weedy species was introduced from Europe. It is found occasionally in the eastern and middle-western states, but has become very abundant in the Pacific coast states. It provides short-season spring forage, but because of its shallow roots and annual habit, does not effectively protect the soil from erosion and is regarded as much inferior to the perennial grasses which it replaces in overgrazed areas. *Bromus mollis* hybridizes with the next species. April—June.

Figure 82

15b Lemmas glabrous. Fig. 83.

Bromus racemosus L.

Annual; tufted; 20—80 cm. tall; panicle stiff, dense, erect. *Bromus racemosus* closely resembles the preceding species and hybridizes with it. It is much less common in the eastern states, however. Starved plants of *B. commutatus* resemble *B. racemosus* but have more open panicles. This is a weedy annual of open ground, introduced from Europe. Low value, short-season spring forage. Spring.

Figure 83

16a Panicle open, the branches spreading or drooping............**17**

16b Panicle dense, erect. Fig. 84.

Bromus rubens L.

Annual; tufted; plants 15—40 cm. tall; panicles 4—8 cm. long. The little reddish bushy panicles look like ragged bristle brushes. Common in the intermountain region and Pacific coast states, on open dry ground. The awns may injure livestock by piercing the facial tissues. Poor, scanty feed. Introduced from the Mediterranean area. March—June.

Figure 84

17a Second glume at least 12 mm. long; lemmas glabrous or sparsely stiff-hairy; awns 2—5 cm. long...............................**18**

17b Second glume 10 mm. long or shorter; lemmas usually softly pubescent; awns 1—2 cm. long. Fig 85.
DOWNY BROME *Bromus tectorum* L.

Annual; tufted; plants 30—60 cm. tall; panicles drooping, 5—15 cm. long. The drooping, reddish panicles are rather ornamental but the plants make poor, sparse feed and the sharp-pointed callus of the lemmas or the awns may penetrate the facial tissues of grazing animals. Of all the weedy European bromes, this is the commonest and most widespread. May—June. *Melica smithii* (see Fig. 190) might be keyed here by the unwary. The plants are not hairy and it is a woodland perennial.

Figure 85

18a Awns 2—3 cm. long; first glume about 8 mm. long. Fig. 86.
Bromus sterilis L.

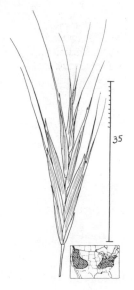

Annual; tufted; culms erect; plants 50—100 cm. tall; leaf sheaths softly hairy or nearly smooth: ligules prominent, membranous, with a lacerated edge; leaf blades soft, sparsely hairy or nearly glabrous; panicles 10—20 cm. long, open, with rather stiffly spreading or drooping branches; spikelets 2.5—3.5 cm. long, with 6—10 florets; lemmas 17—20 mm. long, scabrous or stiff-pubescent; lateral teeth of the lemma about 2 mm. long. The stiff florets, provided with sharp calluses and stiff barbed awns, penetrate the facial tissues of grazing animals. Since the plants are shallow-rooted annuals, they soon dry up and their forage value becomes very low. While very widespread in the United States, *B. sterilis* is nowhere particularly common. Introduced from Europe. April—July.

Figure 86

18b Awns 3—5 cm. long; first glume 1.5—2 cm. long. Fig. 87.
    RIP-GUT GRASS   *Bromus rigidus* Roth

Annual; tufted; plant 40—70 cm. tall; leaf sheaths
and blades coarsely and sparsely hairy; ligules 3—7
mm. long, membranous, with a lacerated margin; panicles dense, with few spikelets, drooping, 7—15 cm.
long, the lower branches only 1—2 cm. long. Some
variants have longer lower panicle branches, hence
a more open panicle. Spikelets usually with 5—7
florets; glumes glabrous; lemmas scabrous or hairy;
lateral teeth 3—5 mm. long; awns strong, barbed. Because of the sharp calluses and strong, stiff awns of
the lemmas, the florets readily penetrate the soft facial
tissues of grazing animals, inflicting bad puncture
wounds around the nose, mouth, and eyes, especially
on sheep. Frequently these become infected, resulting
in pink eye, cancer eye, or other disease conditions.
The common name, rip-gut grass, arises from these
dangerous properties of the florets. Poor, short-season
feed. Introduced from Europe; especially common in
California; rare in the eastern states. April—August.

Figure 87

3. FESTUCA   FESCUE GRASSES

1a Plants perennial, with hard bases; leaves flat or rolled or folded; culms mostly 30 cm. tall or taller; stamens 3; florets opening at time of pollination..2

1b Plants slender, annual, with shallow roots and hair-like leaves; culms usually less than 20 cm. tall; stamens usually 1; florets cleistogamous. Fig. 88.
SIX WEEKS FESCUE   *Festuca octoflora* Walt.

Figure 88

Annual; tufted, seldom over 20 cm. tall. The leaves are borne mostly in a short basal tuft. The plants may be found on poor, usually sandy ground, throughout the United States. Forage value very low. The common name refers to the very short life span. This and a number of small species of other genera, with similar growth habits, go by the name of "six weeks grasses." All may provide short-term emergency feed for range livestock after rains. April—July.

Twelve other similar species of *Festuca* occur in parts of the United States, but are much less common. They are sometimes put in the genus *Vulpia*.

2a Leaf blades flat, soft, the larger ones more than 3 mm. wide; lemmas awnless or nearly so....................................3

2b Leaf blades rolled or folded, firm, less than 3 mm. wide; lemmas awned or awnless..4

3a Spikelets usually less than 10 mm. long, with 5 or fewer florets. Fig. 89.
NODDING FESCUE
Festuca obtusa Biehler

Perennial; tufted; plants 50—100 cm. tall; panicles usually 15—20 cm. long. Nodding fescue is a species found in forests of the eastern half of the United States. The plants grow in small clumps, with somewhat spreading culms and drooping panicles. The spikelets shatter almost before reaching full size, making it difficult to find complete ones. May—September.

A similar but rarer species is *F. paradoxa* Desv., which bear 8—20 spikelets, 4—6 mm. wide, on each lower panicle branch.

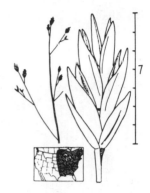

Figure 89

3b Spikelets 8—18 mm. long, with 8—10 florets. Fig. 90.
MEADOW FESCUE
Festuca elatior L.

Perennial; tufted; plants 50—120 cm. tall; leaf blades 4—8 mm. wide; panicle 10—20 cm. long, narrow cylindrical while flowering, but contracted and spikelike afterward. This species was introduced from Europe as a forage plant and has now become widely dispersed in meadows, pastures, roadsides and waste places in the northern states. Forage value good. Also called *F. pratensis*. June—July.

ALTA FESCUE OR KENTUCKY 31 *Festuca arundinacea* Schreb. has similar spikelets. It is a coarse, tough grass with elongated leaf blades with coarse ridges on the upper surface. It is very commonly used as a forage grass in the southeastern states, especially south of the Ohio River and often planted for roadside stabilization; also grown under irrigation in the West. At times it causes lameness and gangrene of the legs in cattle, especially in cold weather (fescue foot disease). This species makes a coarse, bumpy, tough lawn.

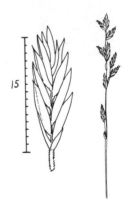

Figure 90

Festuca thurberi Vasey

Perennial; densely tufted; culms rather stout, 60—100 cm. tall. The involute leaves are scabrous. Panicles 10—15 cm. long, the branches separate or paired, as much as 8 cm. long, and bearing spikelets only near their ends. The long ligule is characteristic. Dry rocky slopes, 2500 —3500 m. elevation. Forage value good. July —August.

Figure 91

6a Leaves soft, green. Fig. 92.
GREEN FESCUE   *Festuca viridula* Vasey

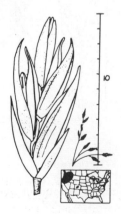

Perennial; in dense tufts; culms 50—100 cm. tall; panicles open, 10—15 cm. long; branches mostly paired, 2—4 cm. long; leaf blades soft, folded or rolled; spikelets with 3—6 florets; lemmas 6—8 mm. long. The lemmas are softer than those of other species of fescue, and frequently have some purplish coloration. Well drained soils in the spruce-fir forests near timberline, mountainsides, parks, and meadows. Green fescue is one of the best forage grasses of the Northwest. It is high in palatability and nutritive value, and is eaten throughout the grazing season by all classes of livestock. July —September.

Figure 92

6b Leaves stiff, bluish. Fig. 93.
  ARIZONA FESCUE; PINEGRASS   *Festica arizonica* **Vasey**

Perennial; densely tufted; culms about 50 cm. tall; leaves stiff, pale, rather scabrous; panicles narrow, 8—20 cm. long, with one or two spreading branches at the base. Open pine forests, mountains of the Southwest. An important grazing grass, closely related to the more northerly *F. idahoensis* (see Fig. 96). July—August.

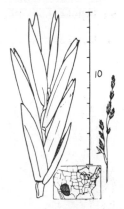

Festuca capillata Lam., commonly called HAIR FESCUE, is a much smaller plant, with spikelets under 5 mm. long, and short, spike-like panicles less than 5 cm. long. It occurs in lawns and waste places in the eastern states and westward to Illinois; Oregon. Introduced from Europe.

Figure 93

7a New leafy shoots arising within the old sheaths; plants forming dense tufts; old sheaths not reddish nor fibrous. **8**
7b New leafy shoots breaking through the bases of the sheaths and spreading at the base, the plants hence forming loose turfs; old basal sheaths reddish brown, finally shredding into brownish threads. Fig. 94
  RED FESCUE   *Festuca rubra* **L.**

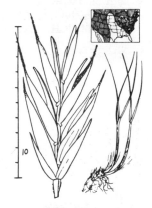

Perennial; tufted; culms 40—100 cm. tall; panicle slender, the short branches ascending. Wet or dry ground; widespread in the eastern United States and in the western mountains. A number of forms of this species are used in lawn mixtures. Chewings fescue and creeping red fescue are among these. Red fescue is native in Europe, Asia, and North Africa as well as North America. Most of the occurrences in the eastern states seem to be introductions, probably in lawn seed mixtures. May—July.

Figure 94

*Festuca occidentali*s Hook. has somewhat similar culm bases but the awns are as long as the lemmas and the long, spreading panicle branches bear spikelets only near their tips. Northwestern states; northern Michigan and Ontario.

8a Leaf blades less than one half the culm length; panicles less than 10 cm. long; plants usually less than 30 cm. tall; widespread in the United States. Fig. 95.
SHEEP FESCUE *Festuca ovina* L.

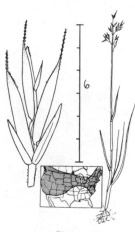

Perennial; tufted; 20—40 cm. tall, with a small, narrow panicle. Since the sterile leafy shoots (innovations) arise within the old sheaths, the plants form dense, bumpy tufts, making this species undesirable as a lawn grass. It frequently appears in old neglected lawns. In mass, the plants have a grayish-green color, but they do not turn brown during dry spells, as bluegrass does. Regarded as good forage in the western mountains. Native also to Europe and Asia. May—June.

Var. *brachyphylla* (Schult.) Piper is a dwarf, high altitude form found above timber line in the western mountains, where it is important for grazing. Culms 5—20 cm. tall.

Figure 95

8b Leaf blades more than one half the culm length; plants 30—100 cm. tall; panicles 10—20 cm. long; in the western mountains. Fig. 96.
BLUEBUNCH FESCUE *Festuca idahoensis* Elmer

Perennial; forming large tufts, the densely crowded slender culms up to a meter in height. The panicles are slender, 10—20 cm. long, usually with a single longer spreading lower branch. The leaves are rough and glaucous, but not as stiff as those of the closely related Arizona fescue (see Fig. 93). Important as a range forage grass. June—August.

Figure 96

4. LEUCOPOA   SPIKE FESCUE

Panicles erect, slender; spikelets unisexual; florets 3—5, the lemmas pointed but awnless, 5-nerved. Fig. 97.

SPIKE FESCUE *Leucopoa kingii* **(S. Wats.) Weber**

Perennial; tufted or sometimes bearing rhizomes; plants 40—100 cm. tall; panicles 7—20 cm. long. Spike fescue has the staminate and pistillate spikelets on separate plants (dioecious). While the spikelets are similar, the pistillate ones have well developed ovaries and abortive anthers, less than 1 mm. long, while the staminate ones have large anthers, about 4 mm. long, and no ovaries. Grazed by cattle and sheep. Dry mountains, at medium altitudes. Also called *Festuca kingii* and *Hesperchloa kingii*.   May—August.

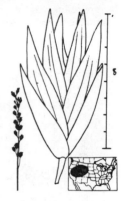

Figure 97

5. LOLIUM   RYEGRASS

The plants of this genus resemble members of the barley tribe (Triticeae) in having symmetrical spikes and have usually been included in that tribe. However, the species of *Lolium* cross freely with *Festuca elatior* and these two genera are closely related. In *Lolium*, the spikelets are placed with one edge against the rachis. Only the exterior glume is developed, except in the spikelet at the very tip of the rachis. Fig. 98.

RYEGRASS   *Lolium perenne* L.

Winter annual or short-lived perennial; culms 30—60 cm. tall; leaves dark green. The lemmas are awnless or nearly so. Ryegrass is much used in lawn seed mixtures, since the seed germinates rapidly and gives a green turf quickly, but the plants tend to die out when hot weather arrives. Lawns, fields, waste places, stream banks. Widely distributed through the United States. This species and the variety listed below furnish good cool-season forage. Introduced from Europe. May —July.

Figure 98

Var. *italicum* Parn. (ANNUAL RYEGRASS). This is barely distinct from the preceding species. It tends to have larger stature, more florets per spikelet, and awned lemmas, but there are many intermediates.

Lolium temulentum L. (DARNEL). Darnel may be recognized by the very long glume, which exceeds the tip of the uppermost lemma. The lemmas are awned. Weed in grainfields and waste places, especially on the Pacific Coast and in the Southeast. This species is sometimes poisonous to livestock and human beings when eaten. Introduced from Europe.

6. PUCCINELLIA   ALKALI GRASS

The grasses of this genus have usually blunt, stiff lemmas with faint parallel nerves, and often a glistening golden or purplish band below the apex. They tend to grow in alkaline or salty places.

1a Panicle pyramidal, open, the lower branches naked near their bases; plants widespread in the United States.................2

1b Panicle dense, short, the branches bearing spikelets to their bases;
plants of the Atlantic Coast. Fig. 99.

Puccinellia fasciculata (Torr.) Bickn.

Perennial; tufted; plants 20—50 cm. tall;
panicles 5—15 cm. long, stiff. Leaf blades
flat, folded, or rolled, 2—4 mm. wide. The
species of *Puccinellia* grow on salty or
alkaline wet soil. The lemmas frequently
have handsome purplish, bronzy, or golden
bands below the apex. This species occurs
in salt marshes along the Atlantic Coast.
June—?

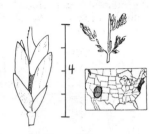

Figure 99

2a Lower panicle branches bent downward; lemmas blunt, broadest
near the apex. Fig. 100.

Puccinellia distans (L.) Parl.

Perennial; tufted; culms erect or decumbent, 20—50 cm. tall; panicle 5—
15 cm. long. The stiffish, drooping lower panicle branches are characteristic.
Leaf blades flat or rolled, usually 2—4
mm. wide. Moist soil. Introduced from
Europe but now widespread in the
United States. June—August.

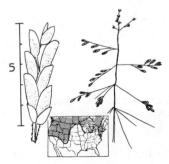

Figure 100

2b Lower panicle branches not bent down; lemmas acute, broadest near the middle. Fig. 101.

ALKALI GRASS   *Puccinellia airoides* (Nutt.) Wats. and Coult.

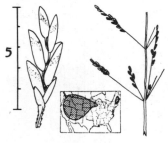

Perennial; tufted; plants 30—60 cm. tall; panicles 10—20 cm. long. Leaf blades flat or rolled, 1—3 mm. wide. Similar to the preceding species, but with narrower lemmas. Native and widely distributed in the West. Sometimes cultivated under the name of Zawadke alkali grass. Also called *P. nuttalliana*. June—August.

Figure 101

7. TORREYOCHLOA

The species given here are marsh and aquatic grasses, usually included in the genus *Glyceria*, from which they differ in having open sheaths and in numerous microscopic characteristics.

1a Lemmas 5-nerved; plants found west of the 100th meridian. Fig. 102.   *Torreyochloa pauciflora* (Presl) Church

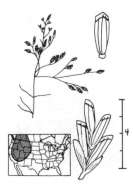

Perennial; tufted; leaf blades usually 10—15 cm. long; 5—15 mm. wide; plants 50—120 cm. tall; panicles drooping, 10—20 cm. long; spikelets 4—5 mm. long, usually with 5—6 florets. The broad lemmas have a purple line near their translucent apex. Marshes, wet meadows, and shallow water, up to timber line. June—September.

Figure 102

1b Lemmas 7-nerved; plants found east of the Mississippi. Fig. 103.
Torreyochloa pallida (Torr.) Church

Perennial; plants weak and sprawling; culms
30—100 cm. long; foliage glabrous; leaf sheaths
split; blades usually 4—8 mm. wide; panicles
open, 5—15 cm. long; spikelets usually 6 7
mm. long, with 4—7 florets; tips of lemmas
thin, membranous, irregular; lemmas 2.5—3
mm. long. This species is found in cold, wet
places, often in shallow water. May—June.

Var. _fernaldii_ is a late-blooming form with
very narrow leaf blades, 1—3 mm. wide. Wet
places and shallow water; Newfoundland to
Pennsylvania, westward to Minnesota and Wisconsin.

Figure 103

8. SCOLOCHLOA

The single species in this genus is a succulent marsh grass, often
missed because its habitats are difficult to visit. The tips of the lemmas are irregularly toothed. Fig. 104.

Scolochloa festucacea (Willd.) Link
Perennial; spreading by thick, elongated
rhizomes; plants 1—1.5 m. tall; panicles
open, 15—20 cm. long; leaf blades usually
5—10 mm. wide. This species is a plant
of marshes and stream borders, where it
often forms large colonies along with
sedges, rushes, and other kinds of aquatic grasses. Furnishes some forage and
marsh hay. Also known as _Fluminea fes-
tucacea_. Late June and early July.

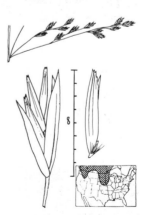

Figure 104

9. SCLEROPOA

The single species present in this country is a rather stiff small grass, resembling small species of *Festuca* or *Poa* and differing mostly in the short, thick, stiff pedicels and branches. Fig. 105.

Scleropoa rigida (L.) Griseb.

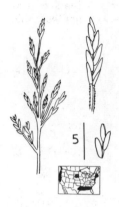

Tufted annual, in small clumps, 10—20 cm. tall, the panicles half the total height, with stiff triangular rachis and short, thick, stiff triangular branches and pedicels; spikelets few, with short 1—3-nerved glumes; florets usually 5—10, the nerves of the lemmas inconspicuous.

Scleropoa is a weedy grass of open dry soil in the eastern, southern, and western states.

Figure 105

10. SCLEROCHLOA

Diminutive annual, with short, thick stiff spikes surrounded by leaves; spikelets falling from the rachis entire; florets 3, the lower 2 fertile; lemmas blunt, stiff, with 5 conspicuous parallel nerves. Fig. 106.

Sclerochloa dura (L.) Beauv.

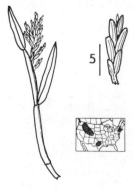

The small tufted plants, less than 10 cm. tall, grow on disturbed dry soil. The rigid inflorescence may have a few short branches at its base. This is an insignificant weed of European origin, found in scattered localities in the intermountain and northwestern states; Texas. The name refers to the stiff, dry, hard texture of the plants. May—June.

Figure 106

HOW TO KNOW THE GRASSES

11. POA   BLUEGRASS

This is a large and important genus of annual and perennial grasses of temperate and cold climates. There is no single character which defines the genus. Many species have a "web" or coma of crimped cottony hairs attached to the callus. The spikelets are usually small, on thin pedicels. The lemmas are never awned or sharp pointed. The 5 nerves of the lemma may be hairy or glabrous. The leaf tips are blunt and cupped or "boat-shaped." Many species are valuable as lawn, pasture, or native forage grasses.

1a Plants producing rhizomes....................................2

1b Plants tufted, without rhizomes............................9

2a Culms round or nearly so in cross section (in pressed specimens, at least the nodes will be round)..........................3

2b Culms strongly flattened, lens-shaped in cross section; spikelets never woolly. Fig. 107.
    CANADA BLUEGRASS   *Poa compressa* L.

Perennial; rhizome-bearing; panicles narrow, 3—7 cm. long. The plants are rather wiry and form looser turf than Kentucky bluegrass. It is somewhat more drought resistant than the former species, but yields less forage. The plants bloom several weeks later than Kentucky bluegrass in the same locality. Introduced from Europe. Mid-May —September.

Figure 107

3a Lemmas completely glabrous or minutely scabrous, or with a small web of cottony hairs (Fig. 108) attached to the callus 4

3b Lemmas pubescent on the keel or nerves, sometimes with a web at the base also........................5

Figure 108

4a Panicles dense, with short branches, the spikelets overlapping; southern plains states or Southeast...........................7b

4b Panicles open, the slender spreading branches naked at the base; western mountains 6b

5a Lemmas pubescent only on the nerves; glabrous between them 6

5b Lemmas pubescent on the nerves and also between them near the base. Fig. 109.
PLAINS BLUEGRASS   *Poa arida* Vasey

Perennial; producing rhizomes; culms 20—60 cm. tall; leaf blades borne mostly near the base of the plant, folded, 2—3 mm. wide; panicle dense, cylindrical, 2—10 cm. long, with short branches; spikelets 5—7 mm. long, the first glume with one nerve; anthers about 1.5 mm. long. Salty or alkaline meadows, up to 3000 m. elevation; an important forage grass on the Great Plains. June—?

Poa glaucifolia Scribn. & Will. is similar. The first glume has 3 nerves; anthers about 2.5 mm. long; panicles more open; herbage glaucous. Moist ground and open woods; Minnesota to British Columbia, to Nevada and New Mexico.

Figure 109

6a Lemmas bearing a web of cottony hairs at the base; sheaths glabrous 7

6b Lemmas without a web of hairs; lower sheaths glabrous or pubescent. Fig. 110.

Poa nervosa (Hook.) Vasey

Perennial; producing rhizomes; culms 30—70 cm. tall, in large, leafy tufts; leaf blades flat or folded; ligules 1—2 mm. long; panicles open, usually 5—10 cm. long, with drooping branches which are naked at the base. The lemmas vary from entirely glabrous to hairy on the nerves or scaberulous. This species is highly variable in the hairiness of both sheaths and lemmas. In common with most of the native and introduced bluegrasses, it is a valuable forage plant for domestic grazing animals and wild herbivores. Dry soil in open woods, intermediate altitudes. May—August.

Figure 110

7a Panicles open, the long branches naked at the bases............8

7b Panicles dense and compact, cylindrical, with overlapping spikelets. Fig. 111.

TEXAS BLUEGRASS *Poa arachnifera* Torr.

Figure 111

Perennial; rhizomes present; plants producing leafy tufts; culms 30—75 cm. tall; leaf blades dark green, 2—4 mm. wide, scabrous on the upper surface; panicles lobed, 5—12 cm. long; spikelets usually with 5—10 florets. The staminate and pistillate spikelets are on different plants, and the two kinds are quite different in appearance. The pistillate panicles are woolly due to the presence of copious cottony webs on the lemmas. The staminate inflorescences are not woolly, their lemmas having only small webs or none at all. The plants are succulent and very leafy; they provide excellent forage in winter and spring. Sometimes cultivated for forage in the southeastern states. April—May.

Poa macrantha Vasey is also dioecious. It is a sand-binder on the coastal dunes from Washington to northern California. The plants have extensive rhizomes and stolons. Spikelets large, about 12 mm. long; webs scanty.

8a Lower panicle branches mostly in pairs; lemmas 3.5—5.4 mm. long; anthers 2.0—3.5 long. Fig. 112.

Poa cuspidata Nutt.

Figure 112

Perennial; rhizomes present; culms 30—50 cm. tall; plants growing in large tufts, with numerous long basal leaves nearly as long as the culms; leaf blades soft, 2—3 mm. wide; upper culm blades very short, rounded to an abrupt tip; panicles 7—12 cm. long, very open, pyramidal, the spikelets all borne at the outer tips of the branches. This is the earliest blooming of all the native eastern grasses, usually beginning to flower in early April in the North. It is a plant of the central and southern Appalachians, where it is commonly found on rocky banks and dry wooded hillsides. Unlike Kentucky bluegrass, which it resembles, it completely lacks aggressive or weedy tendencies.

8b Lower panicle branches mostly in whorls of 5; lemmas 2.4—3.6 mm. long; anthers 1.0—1.8 mm. long. Fig. 113.
KENTUCKY BLUEGRASS   *Poa pratensis* L.

Perennial; rhizomes present; culms 30—100 cm. tall, in dense clumps with numerous sterile leafy shoots (innovations); panicles open, pyramidal, somewhat contracted after flowering. Kentucky bluegrass is one of our most widely distributed introduced grasses and is much used for lawns and pastures in the northern states. It is extensively naturalized in pastures, prairies, roadsides, open woods and waste ground. Introduced from Europe. April—July.

Figure 113

9a Lemmas bearing a web......................................10

9b Lemmas glabrous or pubescent, but without a web.............15

10a Marginal nerves of lemmas pubescent........................11

10b Marginal nerves of lemmas glabrous........................14

11a Lemmas glabrous between the nerves; ligules of upper culm leaves 2.5—7 mm. long...12

11b Lemmas pubescent between the nerves; ligules almost always less than 2 mm. long...13

12a Lemmas greenish-yellow, thin, with prominent intermediate nerves;
sheaths usually scaberulous. Fig. 114.
ROUGH STALK BLUEGRASS; TRIVIALIS   *Poa trivialis* L.

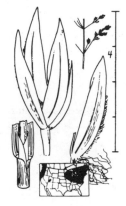

Perennial; tufted; culms 30—100 cm. tall, often somewhat bent or reclining at the base; panicles open, ovoid or pyramidal, the spikelets clustered near the outer ends of the branches; lemmas glabrous or hairy on the lateral nerves. The plants are often found growing wild in wet areas, and the seed is planted in lawn mixtures for shady places. Introduced from Europe. May—June.

Figure 114

12b Lemmas green, usually purple or bronzy at the tip, the intermediate nerves inconspicuous; sheaths smooth. Fig. 115.
Poa palustris L.

Perennial; plants slender, weak, with bent and reclining (decumbent) culm bases; panicles open, pyramidal, with slender, weak branches. The lemmas are usually purple and golden banded near the tip, making them very attractive under the lens. Wet meadows, stream banks, and moist woods; seldom numerous in one place. This species is native to both North America and Eurasia. June—August.

Poa interior Rydb. is very similar to the above, but has erect, tufted culms, small panicles less than 10 cm. long, and short ligules usually 1 mm. long or shorter. Across Canada and south to northern New England, Wisconsin, North Dakota and the high plains and western mountain states.

Figure 115

13a Panicles cylindrical, 10—20 cm. long, the branches 3—6 in a whorl; lower branches drooping.................See *P. sylvestris* under *P. alsodes*, Fig. 116.

13b Panicles pyramidal, 5—10 cm. long, the branches 1—2 at a node, ascending.......See *P. interior* under *P. palustris*. Fig. 115.

14a Upper ligules 3—7 mm. long; sheaths usually scaberulous; intermediate nerves of lemmas conspicuous.....................12a

14b Upper ligules 0.5—2 mm. long; sheaths smooth; intermediate nerves of lemmas inconspicuous. Fig. 116.

Poa alsodes A. Gray

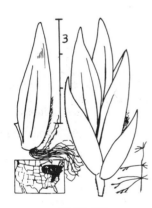

Figure 116

Perennial; tufted; plants slender, 30—60 cm. tall, erect and graceful, with very open, delicate, cylindrical panicles, 10—25 cm. long and half as wide. The slender branches bear a few spikelets near their tips. Cool rocky woods or wooded flood plains in the northeastern states and the Appalachians. May—June.

Poa sylvestris A. Gray is found also in rich woods and resembles this species, but has lemmas which are hairy between the nerves. New York to Wisconsin, southward to Florida and Texas. May—July.

15a Lemmas pubescent between the nerves, the hairs often very short 16

15b Lemmas glabrous between the nerves........................17

16a Panicles very open, the branches slender, spreading, usually in pairs, bearing spikelets only near their outer ends; lemmas with conspicuous long hairs on their keels; eastern forested half of the United States, to Michigan and Texas. Fig. 117.

Poa autumnalis Muhl.

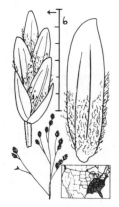

Perennial; tufted; plants delicate, 30—60 cm. tall; panicles 10—20 cm. long and nearly as wide, their branches very slender, bearing a few spikelets near the tips. Leaf blades 2—3 mm. wide, many at the base of the plants. The plants are not, as the name would seem to indicate, autumn blooming. Moist woodlands. June.

Figure 117

16b Panicles usually dense, the branches bearing spikelets nearly to their bases; nerves of lemmas not bearing long hairs; western states, eastward to Minnesota and to the Dakotas. Fig. 118.

Poa scabrella (Thurb.) Benth.

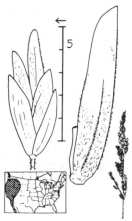

Perennial; tufted; culms 50—100 cm. tall; panicles slender, elongated, with ascending branches. This species and its relatives have lemmas covered, at least near their bases, with short crimped or appressed hairs. A number of very closely related species or forms exist in this group, differing mostly in the shape of the panicle. All are bunch grasses of the western states and are valuable forage grasses at lower and medium altitudes. March—August.

Figure 118

17a Midnerve and lateral nerves of lemmas pubescent.............18
17b Lemmas glabrous or minutely scaberulous, not pubescent.....19
18a Spikelets 6—8 mm. long; keels and marginal nerves of lemmas pubescent; intermediate nerves inconspicuous, not pubescent. Fig. 119.

MUTTON GRASS *Poa fendleriana* (Steud.) Vasey

Perennial; erect, densely tufted bunch grass; leaves mostly basal, stiff and scabrous, folded or rolled, 1—2 mm. wide; culms 30—50 cm. tall, not much exceeding the basal leaves; panicles dense, oblong, 2—7 cm. long, the pale spikelets overlapping. The plants are dioecious but the spikelets of both sexes are similar. Ligules short, less than 1 mm. long. Medium altitude hills and dry forests in the western mountains, from 2300—4000 m. It is regarded as one of the best of western forage grasses, especially for sheep. April— July.

Figure 119

Poa longiligula Scribn & Will. is very similar, but has ligules up to 5—7 mm. long. Range about the same as the preceding species.

18b Spikelets 4—6 mm. long; keels, intermediate nerves, and marginal nerves of lemmas conspicuous, usually all pubescent. Fig. 120.

ANNUAL BLUEGRASS *Poa annua* L.

Annual; tufted. The diminutive light green plants, usually less than 20 cm. tall, are soft, weak, and spreading. Panicles 3—7 cm. long, pyramidal, with short, spreading branches. The plants sometimes grow in shallow water, then becoming long, slender, and rooting at the nodes. This species begins growth in fall or early spring and blooms very early, and may die out when hot weather comes. Some blooming also occurs in fall. Lawns, paths, margins of water and open woods, roadsides. Introduced from Europe.

Figure 120

19a Panicles short, ovoid, 2—8 cm. long; spikelets ovate in outline, about twice as long as wide; glumes and lemmas keeled; nerves of lemmas rather conspicuous..................................20

19b Panicles elongated, cylindrical, 10—15 cm. long; spikelets little keeled, narrowly elliptical in outline, 3 or more times longer than wide, the glumes and lemmas rounded on the back; nerves of lemmas inconspicuous. Fig. 121.

Poa nevadensis Vasey

Perennial; tufted; culms erect, 50—100 cm. tall; sheaths scabrous; panicle narrow, elongated, 10 —15 cm. long. This is one of a group of very similar bunch grasses of the western mountain states. All have slender, elongated spikelets, whose lemmas are not keeled; lemmas glabrous and with inconspicuous nerves. They furnish excellent range forage for wild game animals and domestic livestock. Plains, dry meadows; open or partially wooded mountainsides, from near sea level up to 3700 m. elevation. May—September.

Figure 121

20a Leaf blades scabrous; ligules of culm leaves less than 2 mm. long. Fig. 122.

Poa cusickii Vasey

Perennial; culms in dense bunches, 20—60 cm. tall; basal leaf blades thread-like, very scabrous, about half the length of the culms; ligules usually under 1 mm. long; panicles 3— 8 cm. long, dense, oblong, pale or somewhat purplish. Rocky slopes and sagebrush plains, medium to high altitudes. May—July.

Figure 122

74

20b Leaf blades glabrous; ligules of culm leaves 2—4 mm. long. Fig. 123.

Poa epilis Scribn.

Perennial; culms in small tufts; plants 20 —40 cm. tall; leaf blades of the culms short, flat, 2—3 mm. wide, their ligules 2—4 mm. long; basal leaves long, folded or rolled; panicles on long, thin peduncles; panicles short, dense, oblong, 2—6 cm. long; spikelets about 5 mm. long, usually with 3 florets; lemmas 4—6 mm. long, sometimes scaberulous. *Poa epilis*, sometimes called "skyline bluegrass," is an important high altitude forage grass, usually found above timberline on steep slopes and in mountain meadows. July—August.

About five similar species are to be found at high altitudes in the western mountains, mostly above timberline. They are all dwarf, rarely more than 20 cm. tall.

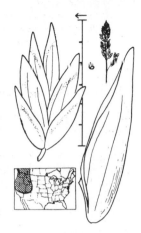

Figure 123

12. BRIZA   QUAKING GRASS

Delicate annual grasses, with spikelets on slender drooping pedicels; florets of the spikelets placed at right angles to the rachilla; lemmas nearly circular, without visible nerves. Fig. 124.

LITTLE QUAKING GRASS   **Briza minor L.**

Annual; tufted; 10—40 cm. tall. The species of *Briza* have very slender pedicels, which allow the drooping spikelets to quiver in any breeze. Ligules 4—5 mm. long. This species is found as a weed in the southern states and often in California. Introduced from Europe. April—May.

Briza media L. is similar, but has larger spikelets. The ligules are about 1.5 mm. long. Northeastern states.

Briza maxima L., with spikelets 10 mm. wide, is the largest species. It is sometimes grown for winter bouquets.

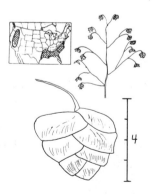

Figure 124

75

13. CATABROSA

Spikelets 1—2-flowered, densely clustered along the panicle branches; lemmas with wide blunt tips and 3 parallel nerves; disarticulation above the glumes and between the florets. Fig. 125.

BROOKGRASS *Catabrosa aquatica* (L.) Beauv.

Perennial. The culms may lie on the ground and root at the nodes for half or more of their length of 10—50 cm. Panicles yellowish, 10—20 cm. long, open, pyramidal. Brookgrass is a soft, succulent grass of wet ground, found in the subarctic and at higher elevations in the western mountains of the United States. The plants make excellent summer feed for livestock. Found also in northern Europe and Asia. June—August.

Figure 125

14. DACTYLIS

Panicles with a few stiff, rigid branches; spikelets nearly sessile in dense, 1-sided tufts at the ends of the branches; glumes and lemmas ciliate on the keels; lemmas pointed or short-awned. Fig. 126.

ORCHARD GRASS *Dactylis glomerata* L.

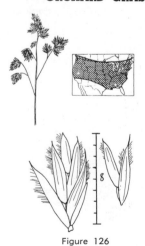

Perennial; tufted; plants 60—120 cm. tall; herbage light green; leaf blades 2—8 mm. wide. The panicle branches spread only at flowering time. The plants grow in large tussocks. They furnish both pasturage and hay, and this species is rather important as a forage grass. It will tolerate partial shade. Introduced from Europe. May—July.

Figure 126

76

15. CYNOSURUS

Inflorescence a dense, somewhat 1-sided panicle with paired fertile and sterile spikelets; sterile spikelets awnless, not disarticulating; fertile spikelets awned, disarticulating into single florets. Fig. 127.

CRESTED DOGTAIL   *Cynosurus cristatus* L.

Perennial; tufted, culms 30—60 cm. tall. The sterile spikelets are paired with fertile ones in the same inflorescence. The sterile spikelet is made up of slender empty awned lemmas. Inflorescence a dense, spikelike panicle. Dogtail is a European grass which has been imported for use in lawn and meadow seed mixtures. It is occasionally found in lawns, pastures and waste places in the eastern states and also in the Pacific Northwest. Apparently it has little value for forage. June—August.

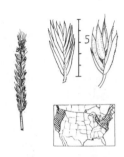

Figure 127

16. LAMARCKIA

Small annual grasses; panicle dense and fluffy, composed of drooping yellow or purplish spikelet clusters; the spikelets of each cluster falling as a unit of 1 perfect and several sterile spikelets; fertile spikelet with a single long-awned perfect floret and a reduced rudimentary one; sterile spikelets composed of numerous awnless empty florets. Fig. 128.

GOLDENTOP   *Lamarckia aurea* (L.) Moench.

Goldentop occurs as a weed and may be cultivated in the southwestern states. February—June.

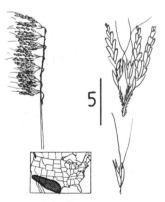

Figure 128

Tribe 3. Aveneae

17. AVENA   OATS

Tufted annuals; panicles and spikelets large; florets usually with stout twisted awns borne on the back of the lemma; florets usually 2 or 3, rather rigid; grain usually retained in the floret; disarticulation above the glumes and between the florets; callus often bearded. Fig. 129.

WILD OATS   *Avena fatua* L.

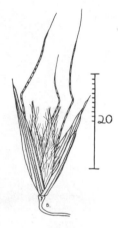

Figure 129

Annual; culms usually 30—100 cm. tall, in small tufts; panicles open, up to 30 cm. long. The spikelets when ripe are open, bell-shaped, with conspicuous protruding bent awns. The scar at the base of the floret is circular and prominent and is usually called a "sucker mouth." Wild oats is distinguished by the hairy lemmas, prominent awns and the sucker mouth. It is widely dispersed in the United States but is most common in the Pacific coast states, where it is a prevalent weed and is sometimes cut for hay. May—August.

Figure 130

Avena sativa L. (CULTIVATED OATS) Fig. 130, differs from wild oats in having lemmas which are glabrous except on the callus, no sucker mouth, and weak, usually straight awns. Widely cultivated and growing from scattered seed on roadsides and waste ground.

78

18. HELICTOTRICHON

Tufted perennials; spikelets with 2—6 florets; lemmas stiff, awned from the back; rachilla hairy; spikelets erect. Fig. 131.

SPIKE OAT   *Helictotrichon hookeri* (Scribn.) Henr.

The species of this genus are sometimes placed in the genus *Avena,* but differ in the characters given above. Plants of this species are found on grasslands and dry mountain slopes in the Rocky Mountains and the northern plains states. July—August.

Figure 131

19. ARRHENATHERUM

Perennial, often with bulbous bases; spikelets with 2 florets, the lower one staminate, with a bent, protruding awn; upper floret perfect, with a short straight awn; spikelets 7—9 mm. long; rachilla prolonged beyond the base of the second floret. Fig. 132.

TALL OATGRASS   *Arrhenatherum elatius* (L.) Mert. & Koch

Perennial; tufted; culms 1—1.5 m. tall; leaf blades 5—10 mm. wide; panicles 15—30 cm. long; narrow and elongated, but with spreading short branches, glumes thin and somewhat translucent. Rarely both florets have bent awns. Tall oatgrass is cultivated in the northern states as a meadow grass and has freely escaped to roadsides and waste ground. Introduced from Europe. May—September.

Figure 132

79

20. DESCHAMPSIA

Tufted, usually perennial grasses; spikelets small, with 2 florets; disarticulation above the glumes and between the 2 florets; rachilla prolonged beyond the second floret as a hairy bristle; awn attached below the middle of the lemma, which has several teeth at the apex. Fig. 133.

HAIRGRASS   *Deschampsia caespitosa* (L.) Beauv.

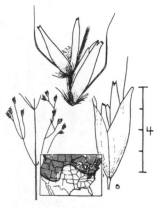

Figure 133

Perennial; tufted; culms slender, 60—120 cm. tall; leaves flat and scabrous, mostly at the base of the plants, 1—4 mm. wide; panicles open, delicate; spikelets often purple. The awns are nearly hidden within the glumes. The lemmas have several minute teeth at their tips. Bogs, wet ground, mountain meadows. An important forage grass in the West. May—July.

Deschampsia flexuosa (L.) Trin. is similar but the awns are strongly bent and protrude from the spikelets. Leaf blades fine and hair-like. Arctic North America, southward to Minnesota and Michigan and southward in the Appalachian Mountains to Georgia; Arkansas and Oklahoma.

21. AIRA

Delicate annual grasses; spikelets small, 2-flowered, the lemmas with 2 teeth at the tip; awn attached to the back of the lemmas below the middle; rachilla not prolonged beyond the base of the upper floret. Fig. 134.

SILVER HAIRGRASS   *Aira caryophyllea* L.

Figure 134

Annual; tufted; culms 10—35 cm. tall. The plants look like delicate little trees with open crowns. The silvery spikelets are closely clustered at the tips of the branches. Dry ground, mostly in the Atlantic and Pacific coastal regions. Introduced from Europe. April—July.

Aira elegans Willd. is similar but the lower floret is awnless or nearly so. Atlantic and Gulf coastal plains; Oregon and California. May—June.

22. TRISETUM

Tufted, usually perennial grasses; spikelets small, 2-flowered; rachilla hairy, extended beyond the base of the second floret as a hairy bristle; lemma 2-toothed at the tip; awn, if present, attached above the middle of the lemma.

1a **Awn short, concealed within the glumes, or absent. Fig. 135.**

Trisetum wolfii Vasey

Perennial; tufted or sometimes with short rhizomes; culms 50—100 cm. tall; leaf blades flat, 2—4 mm. wide, scabrous on the upper surface; panicles dense, cylindrical, yellowish. An important forage grass in moist mountain meadows at mid-altitudes in the western mountains. July—September.

Trisetum melicoides (Michx.) Scribn. is similar but has a loose, drooping panicle. Moist shores and swamps. Newfoundland and New England to Wisconsin. August.

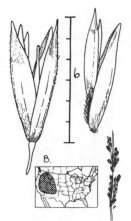

Figure 135

1b **Awn protruding from the glumes, bent and twisted. Fig. 136.**
SPIKE TRISETUM   *Trisetum spicatum* (L.) Richt.

Perennial; tufted; culms 15—50 cm. tall; foliage smooth or finely hairy; panicles spikelike, dense, shaggy with many protruding awns, purplish or golden. An important forage grass at high altitudes, on slopes and in mountain meadows in the western mountains. The plants furnish good forage throughout the growing season, especially for cattle and horses. June—August.

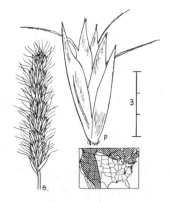

Figure 136

81

23. SPHENOPHOLIS

Annual or perennial tufted grasses; inflorescence usually dense or spikelike; spikelets disarticulating below the glumes, sometimes with a stub of the pedicel attached; first glume narrow, the second usually much broader; florets 2, awnless or awned; rachilla prolonged beyond the second lemma; spikelets very flat.

1a Second floret with a bent awn arising between 2 teeth. Fig. 137.
'Sphenopholis pennsylvanica (L.) Hitch.

Perennial; culms slender and weak, 50—100 cm. tall. The spikelets fall with about half of the pedicel attached. Meadows, swamps, and wet ground. May—June. Formerly called *Trisetum pennsylvanicum.* Recent studies have shown that this species crosses freely with species of *Sphenopholis,* producing sterile awned hybrids which have been called *Sphenopholis pallens.*

Trisetum interruptum Buckl. has similar spikelets but a dense, spikelike panicle. Open dry plains, Texas to Colorado and Arizona. March—May.

Figure 137

1b Both florets lacking awns; lemmas not toothed at the tip. Fig. 138.
WEDGEGRASS   *Sphenopholis obtusata* (Michx.) Scribn.

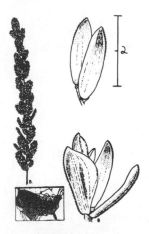

Perennial; tufted; culms 30—100 cm. tall; panicles dense and cylindrical, the branches spreading somewhat at flowering time. The peculiarly shaped glumes are the most characteristic thing about the wedgegrasses. In this species, the second glume is 2—2.5 times longer than its folded width. Succulent and probably good feed, but not occurring in dense stands. May—August.

Var. *major* (Torr.) Erdman has a looser, more open panicle; the second glume is 3—4 times longer than the folded width. Throughout the United States and southern Canada. May—July.

Figure 138

Sphenopholis nitida (Biehler) Scribn. has a slender, open panicle. The upper lemma of each spikelet is visibly scabrous under a lens. Woods, eastern states to Illinois and Texas.

24. KOELERIA

Spikelets flattened; glumes nearly equal, shorter than the florets, the second wider than the first; lemmas awnless or with a very short awn arising at the split tip of the lemma; rachilla joints very short; disarticulation above the glumes and between the florets. Fig. 139.

JUNEGRASS *Koeleria cristata* (L.) Pers.

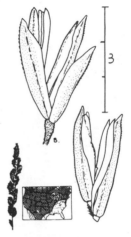

Perennial; tufted; culms 30—60 cm. tall; panicles yellowish or silvery in color, narrowly cylindrical or somewhat lobed. At blooming time the branches spread but later close up again. Spikelets with 2—4 florets. Junegrass is one of the most widely distributed of American grasses. Dry or sandy soil; prairies or open woods. Also found in Eurasia. June—September.

Figure 139

25. HOLCUS

Spikelets 2-flowered, flat, disarticulating below the glumes; foliage soft, velvety. Fig. 140.

VELVET GRASS *Holcus lanatus* L.

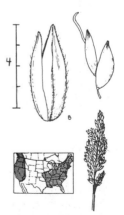

Perennial; tufted; culms 30—60 cm. tall; panicles elliptical, closely flowered. The spikelets have an awnless perfect lower floret and a staminate second floret with a short awn. The entire plant is velvety to the touch. Open moist ground, meadows, thickets. Velvet grass was imported for forage but is rarely cultivated now. The plant has been known to kill livestock under some conditions. Forage value low. Introduced from Europe. June—August.

Figure 140

26. BECKMANNIA

Inflorescence a panicle of short, 1-sided spikes, the circular spikelets in 2 rows along the lower side of the rachis of each spike; spikelets disarticulating below the glumes; floret 1 (2 in the European species). This genus was formerly placed with the Chlorideae because of its inflorescence. Its chromosomes and microscopic characters indicate its proper position is in the Festucoideae. Fig. 141.

SLOUGH GRASS   *Beckmannia syzigachne* (Steud.) Fern.

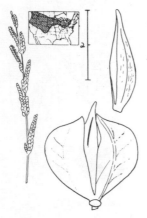

Annual; tufted; plants up to 100 cm. tall. The slender, wand-like panicles of spikes produce large quantities of wrinkled, circular spikelets which shatter from the plants at a touch. Plants rather tender and succulent; forage value good. Wet meadows, shores of ditches and lakes, mostly in the western states. The plants are sometimes cut for hay. July—August.

Figure 141

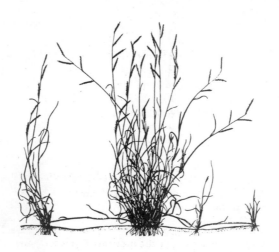

Tribe 4. Phalarideae

27. ANTHOXANTHUM

Glumes longer than florets, and the second about twice as long as the first; florets 3, the lower 2 sterile and awned, the uppermost fertile and awnless, all 3 falling from the glumes as a unit. Fig. 142.

SWEET VERNAL GRASS   *Anthoxanthum odoratum L.*

Perennial; tufted; plants 30—60 cm. tall; panicles yellowish-brown, cylindrical, dense, usually less than 6 cm. long; glumes very thin and delicate. The 2 hairy sterile lemmas are split at the tip and awned from the middle of the back. Sweet vernal grass has the delightful fragrance of coumarin, which persists long after the plants are dried. This species was introduced from Europe, presumably as a meadow plant to add fragrance to hay. Now it is widely established as a weed of roadsides, woods, and meadows, except in the dry parts of the United States. It is one of the earliest of spring grasses, blooming from the middle of April to July in the northern states.

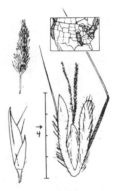

Figure 142

28. HIEROCHLOË

Glumes equal, very thin, longer than the florets; florets 3, the lower 2 usually awnless, staminate; the uppermost floret perfect-flowered, stiff; panicles brownish, shining. Fig. 143.

HOLY GRASS   *Hierochloë odorata (L.) Beauv.*

Perennial; culms 30—60 cm. tall, single or in small tufts, arising from slender creeping rhizomes. Holy grass is an attractive species, with handsome shining golden-brown panicles. The glumes are very thin and translucent. The plants have the sweet, vanillalike scent of coumarin, and were used by the American Indians as material for basketry, and in Europe as perfume in certain religious ceremonies. Moist meadows, bogs, and prairies. April —July.

Figure 143

29. PHALARIS   CANARY GRASS

Inflorescence a dense, cylindrical or thimble-shaped panicle; spikelets strongly compressed, the glumes keeled and usually winged, equal and longer than the concealed florets; fertile terminal floret rigid, shining; falling from the glumes with 2 minute, scale-like sterile florets attached at the base.

1a Plants producing rhizomes; panicles cylindrical and often lobed. Fig. 144.

REED CANARY GRASS   *Phalaris arundinacea* L.

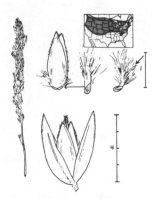

Perennial; plants 60—150 cm. tall, with pale or purplish panicles, 7—16 cm. long. The tall, broadleaved plants furnish considerable forage and are often cut for hay. They form dense colonies in marshes and along ditches. Reed canary grass is now planted for erosion control on farm waterways. Forms with white-striped leaves are sometimes grown for ornament, under the name of "gardeners garters." May—August.

Figure 144

1b Plants tufted, lacking rhizomes; panicle dense, thimble-shaped. Fig. 145.

CANARY GRASS   *Phalaris canariensis* L.

Annual; tufted; culms 30—60 cm. tall; panicles 1—4 cm. long. The strongly winged glumes are striped with green and white lines. This is the species which furnishes the "canary seed" which is fed to caged birds. Occasionally the plants are found growing on trash heaps where the sweepings from bird cages are deposited, but this species apparently does not grow as a truly wild plant in this country. Introduced from Europe. June—August.

A number of other similar species are found in various parts of the United States. None is common or conspicuous.

Figure 145

Tribe 5. Agrostideae

30. AMMOPHILA

Glumes longer than the floret; lemma awnless, bearded on the callus; rachilla prolonged behind the palea as a hairy bristle. Fig. 146.

AMERICAN BEACHGRASS　　*Ammophila breviligulata* Fernald

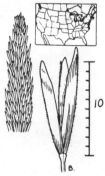

Perennial; spreading by very long, stiff rhizomes. The plants are coarse and tough. Panicles dense and cylindrical, 10—20 cm. long. The plants are highly important sand binders on dunes along the Atlantic Coast and on sand beaches of the Great Lakes. July—September.

A similar species with long ligules, 10—30 mm. long, *Ammophila arenaria*, has been planted on the sand dunes along the Pacific Coast. European.

Figure 146

31. CALAMAGROSTIS　REEDGRASS

Perennials; inflorescence an open or dense panicle; spikelets small, glumes equal, longer than the floret; lemma awned from below the middle, with a tuft of long straight hairs on the callus; rachilla extended behind the palea as a thin, often hairy bristle. This may be concealed by the callus hairs and must be sought carefully.

1a Awn straight, hidden within the glumes; hairs nearly as long as the lemma...2

1b Awn bent sidewise, protruding from the glumes; hairs shorter than the lemma. Fig. 147.

　　PINEGRASS　　　　　　　　*Calamagrostis rubescens* Buckl.

Perennial; culms in tufts, 60—100 cm. tall; plants producing rhizomes; leaf blades scabrous, 2—4 mm. wide, flat or somewhat rolled; panicles dense and cylindrical, 7—15 cm. long, pale or purplish in color; glumes 4—5 mm. long; sterile rachilla joint about 1 mm. long, its hairs about twice as long. While common, pinegrass is low in palatability, especially for sheep, and is little grazed except when young and green. The plants make a strong, tough turf which resists heavy grazing and trampling. Most of the reproduction is by rhizomes. Coniferous forests, up to 3300 m. elevation. June—August.

Figure 147

2a Panicle open, pyramidal, with spreading or drooping elongated branches. Fig. 148.

    BLUEJOINT   *Calamagrostis canadensis* (Michx.) Beauv.

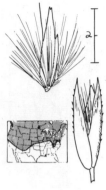

Perennial; culms slender, in small tufts, 60—150 cm. tall; plants producing many long creeping rhizomes. The panicles vary from rather dense to loose, pyramidal, and nodding. Bluejoint is a very widespread and common species found in marshes and wet ground. While rather tough, it furnishes a good deal of forage and is sometimes cut for marsh hay in the North Central States. June—August.

Figure 148

2b Panicle dense, cylindrical, with short, erect branches. Fig. 149.

                                    Calamagrostis inexpansa Gray

Perennial; culms in tufts, 40—120 cm. tall; plants producing rhizomes. The dense, cylindrical panicle may be pale or purplish. The leaf blades are rough to the touch and usually rolled; ligules 4—7 mm. long. Marshes and wet meadows, apparently sometimes on dry soil in the western mountains. June—July.

Figure 149

32. AGROSTIS   BENTGRASS

Inflorescence an open or dense panicle; spikelets small; glumes equal, longer than and concealing the floret; lemma usually awnless, thin and delicate; palea short or obsolete, thin; rachilla not prolonged. Many species; some cultivated for lawns, pastures, and putting greens.

1a Palea at least half as long as the lemma; plants often with rhizomes or stolons..2

1b Palea absent or less than ¼ as long as the lemma; plants tufted, lacking rhizomes or stolons....................................4

2a Plants with erect stems; panicles open, pyramidal..............3

2b Plants with creeping stolons, rooting at the nodes and forming flat mats; rhizomes absent; panicle narrow, the branches closing up after the flowering period. Fig. 150.
   CREEPING BENT   *Agrostis palustris* Huds.

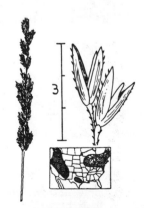

Perennial; low, spreading by numerous fine leafy stolons. This species is much used for golf greens and fine lawns, but requires frequent cutting and watering to produce a good turf, and the plants are subject to several serious diseases. New lawns are usually produced by planting pieces of chopped turf, which take root and spread to form a continuous sod. Reproduction by seed is also possible, but seed of many strains is very scarce or unobtainable. Various forms of this species are known as seaside bent, Coos Bay bent, Washington bent and Metropolitan bent. Marshes, especially along seacoasts, wet ground around streams, springs, lakes, and ditches. Also known from Europe and Asia. June—September.

Figure 150

3a Ligules 1—2 mm. long; leaf blades 1—3 mm. wide. Fig. 151.
   BROWNTOP   *Agrostis tenuis* Sibth.

Perennial; plants 20—40 cm. tall; rhizomes absent but short stolons sometimes present; leaf blades very narrow; ligules on sterile shoots about 1 mm. long, on the culms up to 2 mm. long; panicles usually 5—10 cm. long, brownish, open and delicate, the spikelets all near the outer tips of the branches. *Agrostis tenuis* is cultivated as a lawn and pasture grass and is sometimes referred to as Rhode Island bent, Prince Edward Island bent, Colonial bent, New Zealand bent, or Astoria bent. The plants are occasionally found growing wild in regions where browntop is cultivated. Some forms possess lemmas which bear a delicate awn attached near the base. Introduced from Europe. June—July.

Figure 151

3b Ligules 3—7 mm. long; leaf blades 2—6 mm. wide. Fig. 152.
   REDTOP   *Agrostis alba* L.

Perennial; culms up to 1—1.5 m. tall; numerous creeping rhizomes present; panicle pyramidal, with rather dense whorls of branches, flowering to their bases. Redtop is one of our most important meadow grasses, and is also used in lawn seed mixtures. Roadsides, meadows, waste ground; very widely naturalized. Introduced from Europe. June—August.

Figure 152

4a Panicle narrow, with the short branches bearing spikelets nearly to their bases..**5**

4b Panicle open, the spreading branches bearing spikelets at their outer ends only..**6**

5a Slender alpine plants; leaf blades 5 cm. long or shorter, 1—2 mm.
wide; ligules 1—2 mm. long; panicles usually less than 5 mm. wide.
Fig. 153.

Agrostis variabilis Rydb.

Perennial; tufted; culms 10—20 cm. tall; panicles small, 2—6 cm. long; spikelets about 2.5
mm. long; lemmas about 1.5 mm. long; palea
very short. High altitudes in the mountains,
usually above timberline along creeks and on
slopes. Forage value good. July—August.

Agrostis humilis Vasey. Similar but smaller,
differing from the above chiefly in having a
palea about 2/3 as long as the lemma; plants
5—15 cm. tall; panicles purple, slender, 1—3
cm. long. Excellent forage. Bogs and mountain meadows above timberline, Montana and
Washington to Colorado and Nevada. July—
August.

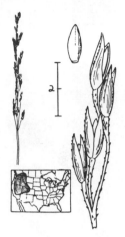

Figure 153

5b Stouter plants of medium and low altitudes; longer leaf blades
8—10 cm. long; ligules 3—6 mm. long; panicles usually 1—several
cm. wide. Fig. 154.
SPIKE REDTOP   *Agrostis exarata* Trin.

Perennial; tufted; culms 20—120 cm. tall;
panicles spikelike, either thin, or thicker and
somewhat lobed. Lemma sometimes awned.
This is one of the most important western
range grasses. It is palatable to both domestic livestock and wild grazing animals.
Usually on moist ground, in meadows, along
streams, and in open woodlands. July—August.

Figure 154

6a Panicles with long, slender main branches which branch again only on the outer half. Fig. 155.
TICKLEGRASS   *Agrostis scabra* **Willd.**

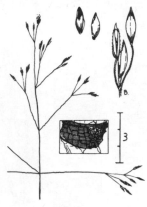

Figure 155

Perennial; culms slender, 20—80 cm. tall; leaf blades threadlike, in dense tufts at the base of the culms; panicles delicate, readily breaking away from the plants and blown by the wind as tumbleweeds. Forage value fair. Ticklegrass is a very widespread species, on open ground or in partial shade, especially on moist soil. June—September.

Agrostis hyemalis (Walt.) B. S. P. is similar but has spikelets bunched at the tips of the branches. Atlantic Coastal Plain and lower Mississippi Valley. It blooms earlier, in May and early June.

6b Main panicle branches branching again below the middle. Fig. 156.
Agrostis perennans (Walt.) Tuck.

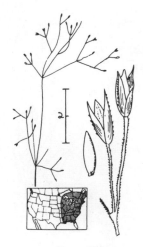

Figure 156

Perennials; tufted; culms 20—80 cm. tall; panicles usually delicate and lace-like, especially in shade-grown plants. Lemmas rarely awned. Dry open fields and woodlands. July—October.

Agrostis oregonensis Vasey is similar, but larger and more vigorous. Marshes; Montana to British Columbia, southward to Wyoming and California.

33. GASTRIDIUM

Panicle dense and spikelike, bristly; glumes swollen at the base, with long, beak-like tips; rachilla extended behind the palea as a minute bristle. Fig. 157.

NIT GRASS   *Gastridium ventricosum* **(Gouan) S. & T.**

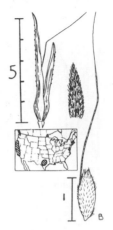

Annual; tufted, shallow-rooted; culms 20—55 cm. tall; panicles dense, cigar-shaped, with glossy silvery or yellowish spikelets. The minute floret is concealed by the glumes. Weed of fields and waste places, common on the Pacific Coast. Introduced from Europe. May—July.

Figure 157

34. POLYPOGON

Panicles dense, soft, silky; spikelets small, with long-awned glumes and lemma; disarticulation below the spikelets, which fall with a short bit of the pedicel attached. Fig. 158.

RABBITFOOT GRASS   *Polypogon monspeliensis* **(L.) Desf.**

Annual; tufted; usually 15—50 cm. tall; panicles dense, often somewhat lobed, densely covered with soft, silky yellowish awns. Rabbitfoot grass is rather widely distributed in the United States, but is most common in the West, at low altitudes. Frequently found on seepy wet ground around springs or on banks of streams. Weedy; forage value low. Introduced from Europe. May —October.

Figure 158

93

35. SCRIBNERIA

Inflorescence a slender spike or reduced panicle; spikelets 1 per node, pressed against the rachis; glumes equal, concealing the floret; floret only ¼ to ½ as long as the glumes; rachilla prolonged behind the palea; awn protruding from the glumes; stamen 1. Fig. 159.

Scribneria bolanderi (Thurb.) Hack.

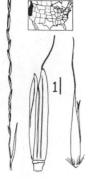

Slender annual grass; among shrubs; plants up to 30 cm. tall, rare or inconspicuous. Lower elevations in the mountains, Washington to California. Spring.

This odd little grass was placed in the barley tribe by Hitchcock. The occasional presence of branches in the inflorescence suggests that it should not be placed in this tribe, but its microscopic characters place it in the festucoid subfamily.

Figure 159

36. LIMNODEA

Spikelets in slender panicles, 1-flowered, disarticulating below the glumes; glumes equal, longer than the floret; lemma bearing a slender protruding awn attached below the split tip; rachilla prolonged behind the palea. Fig. 160

Limnodea arkansana (Nutt.) Dewey

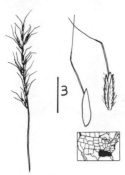

Tufted annual; plants 20—40 cm. tall. Dry open soil; spring.

Figure 160

37. CINNA

Inflorescence a drooping panicle; spikelets disarticulating below the glumes; lemma short-awned; rachilla extending beyond the base of the floret as a minute bristle. Fig. 161.

WOODREED   *Cinna arundinacea* L.

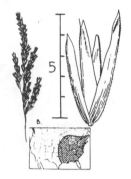

Perennial; culms in small tufts, 100- 150 cm. tall; panicles large, 15—30 cm. long, drooping, the very flat spikelets shining, overlapping. The leaves are sometimes over 1 cm. wide. This common woodland grass is found in moist forests. August—October.

Cinna latifolia (Trevir.) Griseb. has smaller spikelets, less than 4 mm. long. Arctic America, southward through most of the United States except the southeastern states.

Figure 161

38. ALOPECURUS

Panicle dense and spikelike; spikelets freely dropping from the plant, the disarticulation below the glumes, which are equal, strongly keeled, and joined near the base; lemma with edges united near the base; palea absent; awn attached below the middle of the lemma.

1a Spikelets about 5 mm. long; panicles 7—10 mm. in diameter; awns protruding. Fig. 162.

MEADOW FOXTAIL   *Alopecurus pratensis* L.

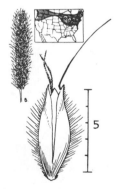

Perennial; tufted; culms 30—80 cm. tall. The panicles resemble those of timothy but the lemmas have protruding bent awns and the spikelets fall off at a touch when ripe. This genus is one of very few having united glumes. Meadow foxtail is sometimes cultivated as a forage grass in the northern states and found growing wild in meadows and waste ground. Introduced from Europe. May—June.

Figure 162

1b Spikelets 2—3 mm. long; panicles 4—5 mm. in diameter; awns concealed in the glumes. Fig. 163.

Alopecurus aequalis Sobol.

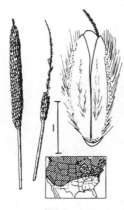

Perennial; culms weak and sprawling, 15—60 cm. long; leaf blades 1—4 mm. wide; panicles cylindrical, shattering very readily; 2—7 cm. long. The plants are frequent on wet ground in swamps or along small streams. Succulent and probably good forage. May—June.

Alopecurus carolinianus Walt. has similar spikelets but with a bent awn protruding from the glumes. Tufted, erect annual. Throughout most of the United States. April—June.

Figure 163

39. PHLEUM

Panicle dense, spikelike, stiff; spikelets very flat and overlapping, fringed with short hairs; midnerve of each glume extended into a short, stiff awn; florets concealed within the glumes. Fig. 164.

TIMOTHY   *Phleum pratense* L.

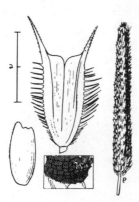

Perennial; tufted, the culms 50—100 cm. tall, often with swollen, bulb-like bases. The dense, cylindrical panicles are stiff and somewhat bristly. Timothy is one of the important hay meadow grasses in the northern states, and is also very widely established in the wild in the moister portions of the country. June—July.

Phleum alpinum L. (ALPINE TIMOTHY), with short, plump, dark colored panicles, occurs in wet mountain meadows at high altitudes in the West and from Greenland to Alaska.

Figure 164

40. MILIUM

Panicle open and drooping; glumes equal, covering and concealing the hard, shining, dorsally-compressed floret; disarticulation above the glumes. Fig. 165.

Milium effusum L.

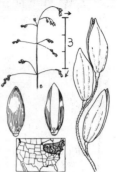

Perennial; culms in small tufts, up to 150 cm. tall. Foliage smooth, the leaf blades 8—15 mm. wide. The panicles are 10—20 cm. long, very open, cylindrical, with short drooping branches. The dorsally-compressed floret greatly resembles that of species of *Panicum*, but the disarticulation above the glumes places it with the Agrostideae. Cool, moist woods. May—July.

Figure 165

Tribe 6. Triticeae

41. AGROPYRON   WHEATGRASS

Tufted or rhizomatous grasses; inflorescence a balanced spike; spikelets 1 at each node, laterally flattened against the rachis; florets several; disarticulation above the glumes and between the florets; lemmas acute or awned; grain usually retained in the floret.

1a Plants producing creeping rhizomes..........................2

1b Plants lacking rhizomes......................................3

2a **Leaves bluish glaucous, often inrolled; upper leaf surface furrowed, with 7—14 ridges across the width. Fig. 166.**
     WESTERN WHEATGRASS   *Agropyron smithii* **Rydb.**

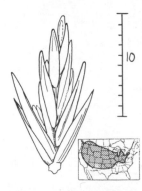

Perennial; culms 30—60 cm. tall; leaves heavily glaucous, so that patches of the plants have a conspicuous blue or silvery color when viewed from a distance. Spikes slender, with erect spikelets. This is essentially a plant of the mountain and plains states of the West, but is occasionally found farther east. In the western parts of its range it is a source of forage on moist alkaline soil. Farther east, it grows on dry uplands, railroad embankments, etc. June —August.

Figure 166

2b **Leaves flat, usually green; upper surface of blades finely nerved, with 25—40 nerves across the width. Fig. 167.**
     QUACKGRASS   *Agropyron repens* **(L.) Beauv.**

Perennial; with extensive creeping rhizomes; culms 50—100 cm. tall; leaves flat, green, often hairy on the upper surface; spike slender, with erect spikelets. Some of the plants have awned lemmas. Quackgrass is one of the worst grass weeds in the northern states. It produces good forage but is not intentionally planted as a crop. Waste ground, roadsides, fields and meadows. Introduced from Europe. May— July.

Figure 167

3a Spikelets erect, pressed against the rachis; rachis joints at least 5 mm. long..4

3b Spikelets spreading away from the rachis, overlapping; rachis joints about 1 mm. long. Fig. 168.
   CRESTED WHEATGRASS *Agropyron desertorum* (Fisch.) Schult.

Perennial; tufted; culms 60—100 cm. tall. The strongly divergent spikelets distinguish this species from all others of this genus. Crested wheatgrass is a recent introduction from the Old World and has proved very useful for regrassing abandoned crop lands and depleted ranges in the northern great plains states. A valuable forage species. Formerly known as *Agropyron cristatum*. June—August.

Figure 168

4a Lemmas awnless or with straight awns. Fig. 169.
   Agropyron trachycaulum (Link) Malte

Perennial; tufted; culms 50—100 cm. tall; spikes and spikelets slender; glumes conspicuously nerved. Awned and awnless forms occur, often in the same stand of plants. This is an important forage species in the western mountains. Moist grassland and open woods. As here discussed, this species includes what are called *A. pauciflorum* (awnless) and *A. subsecundum* (awned). June—September.

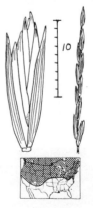

Figure 169

4b Lemmas with strongly bent awns. Fig. 170.
    BLUEBUNCH WHEATGRASS *Agropyron spicatum* (Pursh) S. & S.

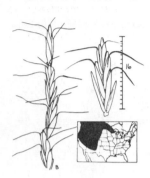

Perennial; tufted; culms 60—100 cm. tall. The spikes are slender and delicate. Sheaths smooth; blades 1—4 mm. wide, hairy on the upper surface. This species is one of the most abundant and important forage species of the northwestern states, and is readily eaten at all seasons and by all kinds of livestock. Dry plains and open mountain slopes. May—August.

Figure 170

42. TRITICUM   WHEAT

Tufted annual grasses; inflorescence a balanced spike; spikelets 1 per node; bracts blunt-tipped, short and broad, sometimes awned; disarticulation above the glumes and between the florets; grain in our species dropping from the floret when ripe. This genus is closely related to *Agropyron*, differing mostly in the floret shape and the free grain. Fig. 171.

WHEAT   *Triticum aestivum* L.

Wheat is the most extensively cultivated of the small grains and may be found growing in fields, waste places and roadsides as the result of seed being scattered accidentally. Some varieties of wheat have awned lemmas, other are awnless. Two primitive kinds of wheat, EMMER and SPELT, have spikes with a brittle rachis which breaks into individual joints at maturity. Both are occasionally grown as feed grains in dry regions. All introduced from the Old World. Cultivated wheat was derived from ancient hybridizations of primitive wheats and goatgrass (*Aegilops*).

Figure 171

43. SECALE   RYE

Cultivated tufted annual; spike slender; spikelets 1 per node; glumes short, awnless; florets 2, the rachilla prolonged beyond the second; lemmas strongly folded, with a row of short rigid bristles along the keel; disarticulation above the glumes; grain falling free at maturity. Fig. 172.

RYE *Secale cereale* L.

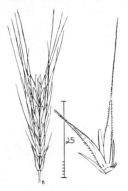

Rye resembles wheat in general appearance, but has a more slender spike. The lemmas are strongly V-shaped in cross section and have rows of vicious, upwardly-pointed barbs along keel and margins. Rye culture is confined mostly to the northern states. The plants may be found scattered along roads and in waste places in regions where it is grown. Introduced from Europe. Summer. Elongated blackish horns protruding from spikelets are ergot, a poisonous fungus used in medicine.

Figure 172

44. AEGILOPS

Annual weeds; inflorescence a cylindrical balanced spike; spikelets 1 per node, fitting against the rachis joint, which is thickened at its upper end; rachis disarticulating into individual internodes when ripe, each falling with the attached spikelet; florets 2—5; awns conspicuous. Fig. 173.

GOATGRASS *Aegilops cylindrica* Host

Annual; tufted; 40—60 cm. tall; much branched from the base, one plant bearing as many as 60 spikes; spikes 5—10 cm. long; joints of the rachis 6—8 mm. long, the spikelets slightly longer and fitting closely into the contour of the joints; spikelets glabrous or hairy, with 2—5 florets; lower spikelets nearly awnless, the upper ones bearing awns up to 5 cm. long; glumes thick and stiff, bearing a pronounced tooth at one side of the awn. Goatgrass was presumably introduced into the Middle West in Turkey wheat brought to the United States by Russian immigrants in the 1870's. The plants are winter-annual, beginning growth in the fall and seeding out from May to July. They crowd out wheat when they are numerous. The seeds travel as contaminants in wheat seed.

Aegilops triuncialis L. is similar but has 3 awns on each glume. It is a bad weed on range land in California; introduced from Europe.

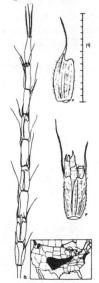

Figure 173

45. ELYMUS   WILD RYE

Tufted or rhizomatous perennials or rarely annuals; inflorescence a balanced spike; spikelets usually 2 per node (rarely 1 or more than 2), placed laterally to the rachis, but the rachilla deformed so that the back of the first lemma is outward; florets 2 or more, usually awned; disarticulation above the glumes and between the florets.

1a **Spikes very broad; spikelets with 1 fertile floret and a rudiment; awn 5—10 cm. long; nearly leafless annual. Fig. 174.**
   MEDUSA-HEAD   *Elymus caput-medusae* L.

This wiry annual weed has bristly spikes with very long awns. These may cause dangerous puncture wounds in grazing live-stock. The plants are fibrous and furnish very poor forage, while they compete aggressively with better grasses. Northwestern states, to California. Introduced from Europe. Spring.

Figure 174

1b **Spikes much longer than broad; spikelets with several fertile florets; awns absent or less than 4 cm. long; perennials, leafy**..........2
2a **Plants lacking rhizomes or rarely with short, thick ones**..........3
2b **Plants producing slender creeping rhizomes; ligule 1 mm. long. Fig. 175.**

                                        Elymus triticoides Buckl.

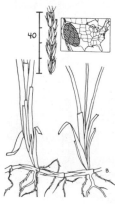

Perennial; culms usually 60—120 cm. tall, single or in small tufts, forming large patches by means of the long, slender rhizomes. The leaves are harsh, stiff, bluish-glaucous and often rolled. Damp or saline soils, open ground. Sometimes part of the spike will have only a single spikelet at a node. Seven other species of *Elymus* produce extensive rhizomes. They are mostly plants of sand dunes along the oceans or in river valleys. May—August.

Figure 175

3a Glumes very narrow, widest at the base and tapering upward, less than 1 mm. broad...4

3b Glumes flattened, wider near the middle than at the base, the middle portions with several nerves................................5

4a Lemmas awnless or with awns shorter than the body of the lemma; plants of the Great Plains and western mountains and deserts. Fig. 176.

    GIANT WILD RYE   *Elymus cinereus* Sribn. & Merr.

Perennial; tufted; rarely with short, thick rhizomes; culms about 1 m. tall; leaves thick, stiff, flat or rolled; ligules 3—6 mm. long; spikes 15—30 cm. long. This is an important forage grass of dry plains, sand hills, and ditches in the western states. May—August.

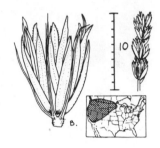

Elymus condensatus Presl is a very tall species, up to 3 m. high, with large, often compound spikes, up to 50 cm. long and 3 cm. thick. It grows along the Pacific Ocean beaches in California.

Figure 176

4b Lemmas with awns at least as long as the body; plants of woodlands; eastern states and westward to Wyoming and Texas. Fig. 177.

                                   Elymus villosus Muhl.

Perennial; tufted; culms slender, 60—100 cm. tall; leaf blades thin and dark green, their upper surfaces velvety to the touch; spikes 5—12 cm. long; spikelets usually densely hairy; glumes 12—20 mm. long; lemmas 7—9 mm. long, with an awn 1—3 cm. long. Stream banks, thickets, and moist woods. June—August.

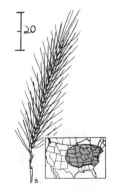

Figure 177

5a Spikes loose and curved; awns strongly recurved when dry; bases of glumes thin and flat. Fig. 178.
CANADA WILD RYE   *Elymus canadensis* L.

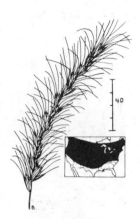

Perennial; tufted; culms erect or arching, bearing large, bristly spikes up to 25 cm. long. The lemmas are rather coarsely hairy. Canada wild rye is our most widespread species and is common over much of its range. It has been experimentally planted for forage production in the Middle West. Prairies, open ground, rocky banks and open woods. July—September.

Elymus riparius Wiegand is very similar but has awns which are straight even when mature and dry. The lemmas are scabrous, not hairy as in *E. canadensis*. Quebec to North Carolina, west to Nebraska and Arkansas.

Figure 178

5b Spikes stiff and straight; awns straight; bases of glumes round in cross section, hard and smooth. Fig. 179.
VIRGINIA WILD RYE   *Elymus virginicus* L.

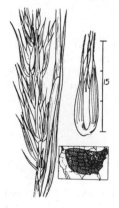

Perennial; tufted; culms stiffly erect, 60—120 cm. tall; the base of the spike often hidden in the uppermost sheath. The "bowlegged" glumes are a good mark of recognition. Awned and awnless forms, as well as forms with smooth or hairy lemmas, are known. The plants are extremely variable in size and growth habit. The bases of the glumes are usually yellowish. Woods, thickets, stream banks, open ground. June—September.

Figure 179

46. HYSTRIX

Inflorescence a balanced spike of awned spikelets which spread at right angles to the rachis; 1—4 spikelets per node; glumes absent or reduced to short stubs; disarticulation below and between the florets. The genus is closely related to *Elymus*. Fig. 180.

BOTTLEBRUSH   *Hystrix patula* Moench

Perennial, in small tufts; culms slender, 60—120 cm. tall. Spikes 8—15 cm. long, very open, because of the spreading spikelets. Leaf sheaths smooth or hairy; blades usually 7—15 mm. wide. This is a characteristic grass of damp woodlands throughout the eastern wooded section of the country. In var. *bigeloviana* (Fern.) Deam, the lemmas are hairy. June—August.

Figure 180

47. HORDEUM   BARLEY

Annual or perennial tufted grasses; inflorescence a balanced spike, the rachis (except in cultivated barley) breaking up at the base of each internode when ripe, and carrying at the apex of the internode a trio of spikelets; spikelets 3 at each node, the central one fertile, the lateral 2 usually reduced and sterile; floret 1, the rachilla of the central spikelet prolonged behind the palea.

1a Rachis of spikes separating at maturity into individual joints, each bearing 3 spikelets; wild plants..................................2

1b **Rachis of spikes not separating into joints; cultivated annual. Fig. 181.**

BARLEY *Hordeum vulgare* L.

Annual; tufted; culms usually 60—120 cm. tall; leaf blades flat, usually 5—15 mm. wide, with prominent auricles; spikes stiff and erect; spikelets 3 at each node of the rachis; each spikelet with a single fertile floret; glumes awned; lemma with a stout awn, usually 10—15 cm. long and very scabrous; rachilla prolonged behind the palea as a small bristle. In the hooded barleys, the lemmas lack awns but bear minute abortive extra lemmas at their tips, in inverted position. Common strains of barley are 6-rowed, that is, all 3 spikelets at each node develop grains. There are also 2-rowed barleys, in which only the central spikelet of each trio develops a grain. Barley is cultivated for the grain, which is used for human food (pearl barley, cereals), for production of malt, and for livestock feed. It is grown principally in the Middle West and in the Great Valley of California. Stray plants may grow from scattered seed, but barley is never found growing as a truly wild plant.

Figure 181

2a **Awns mostly 5—8 cm. long; plants perennial. Fig. 182.**

FOXTAIL BARLEY *Hordeum jubatum* L.

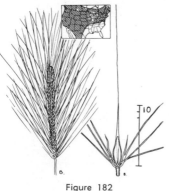

Tufted; culms 30—60 cm. tall. The bushy spikes are 5—10 cm. long, and because of the spreading awns, about as wide. When still fresh, the awns often have a purplish or pink sheen. When the spikes are ripe, they break up into segments, each with a sharp-edged rachis joint at its base, and a trio of spikelets at its apex. Only the central spikelet is fertile, and the lateral two are reduced to long awns. The spike-segments are able to penetrate clothing, wool, or flesh, causing puncture wounds, especially around the faces of animals. For this reason, foxtail barley is undesirable as a forage plant. Open ground, mostly in the midwestern and western states. May—August.

Figure 182

2b Awns less than 2 cm. long; plants annual. Fig. 183.
    LITTLE BARLEY   *Hordeum pusillum* Nutt.

Annual; culms 10—35 cm. tall, in small tufts. Both glumes of the central spikelet and the inner one of each lateral spikelet are broadened above the base. The plants furnish some early season forage, but are rejected by livestock after the spikes emerge. Plains and open ground; common in the Middle West and westward. February—July.

Hordeum brachyantherum Nevski is similar, but all of the glumes are narrow. Western mountain states, not common in the East.

Hordeum leporinum Link has thicker spikes which are nearly square in cross section and partially hidden in the uppermost sheath. Glumes of the central spikelet hairy on the edges. Mostly in the plains and mountain states. Introduced from Europe.

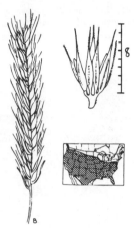

Figure 183

48. X AGROHORDEUM

Sterile hybrids of *Agropyron* and *Hordeum* species, having several florets per spikelet as in *Agropyron*, and the disarticulating rachis of *Hordeum*. Fig. 184.

X *Agrohordeum macounii* (Vasey) Lepage.
This hybrid is commonly found on disturbed soil, along roads or in weedy pastures, where its parents, *Agropyron trachycaulum* and *Hordeum jubatum* grow together. The spikes commonly have 2 spikelets at the lower nodes. Above this there may be single spikelets with 3 glumes and normal single spikelets. No seed is produced, but the plants may gradually form sizable clumps. Iowa and Minnesota to Alaska and California. Sometimes called *Elymus macounii*, but not belonging to that genus.

Figure 184

49. X ELYHORDEUM

Sterile hybrids between various species of *Elymus* and *Hordeum*, having the spikelets like those of *Elymus* but the disarticulating rachis of *Hordeum;* tufted perennials; inflorescence a balanced spike; spikelets 3 at each node, several-flowered, similar. Nine hybrids of this parentage have been found in various parts of North America. *Hordeum jubatum* is one parent of most of these, and they resemble this species in general aspect. Such hybrids should be looked for in disturbed sites where the parent species grow together.

50. SITANION

Tufted perennials; inflorescence a balanced spike, the rachis disarticulating at the base of each internode; spikelets 2 at each node, several-flowered, long-awned, falling attached to the apex of the thin, sharp-edged rachis joint. Fig. 185.

SQUIRRELTAIL   *Sitanion hystrix* (Nutt.) J. G. Smith

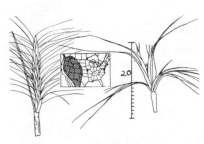

Figure 185

Culms 10—50 cm. tall, erect or spreading. The glumes bear 1 or 2 long, bent awns. The plants resemble *Hordeum jubatum* but the several florets per spikelet and 2 spikelets per node separate it from that species. The rachis joints bearing the awned spikelets may penetrate the facial parts of grazing animals, causing serious inflammation, pink eye, etc. Fair forage when seed heads are not present. Dry woods and grasslands. April—September.

Sitanion jubatum J. G. Smith is similar but has 3 or more awns on each glume. Intermountain and Pacific coast states.

Tribe 7. Meliceae

51. MELICA

Perennials, often with bulbous bases or short rhizomes; sheaths with united edges; inflorescence a panicle; spikelets disarticulating below the glumes or above the glumes and between the florets; upper florets sterile and enwrapping each other. Awned species are similar to *Bromus* but differ in having rudimentary upper florets.

1a Spikelets disarticulating below the glumes and falling entire at maturity 2

1b Spikelets disarticulating above the glumes and between the florets 5

2a Rudimentary lemmas forming a pointed, cigar-shaped structure . . 3

2b Rudimentary lemmas forming a blunt, club-shaped or bell-shaped structure 4

3a Glumes reaching nearly to the tip of the spikelet; spikelets V-shaped. Fig. 186.

Melica stricta Bolander

Perennial; tufted; plants 15—60 cm. tall; panicle slender, almost unbranched, raceme-like. All of the species of *Melica* have thin, translucent glumes and firmer lemmas. In this species, the glumes frequently have considerable purple coloration. Leaf blades scabrous, hairy on the top, 1—3 mm. wide. Rocky and gravelly slopes in the mountains. Late May—August.

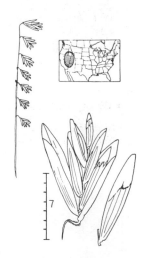

Figure 186

3b Glumes less than 2/3 as long as the entire spikelet; spikelets narrow, cylindrical. Fig. 187.

Melica porteri Scribn.

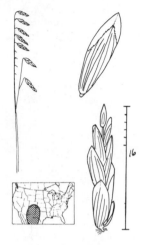

Perennial; tufted; 50—100 cm. tall; inflorescences slender and racemelike, 15—20 cm. long, the branches ascending; spikelets mostly drooping to one side; pedicels hairy; spikelets green or brownish, not purple, 10—15 mm. long, with 4—5 florets; lemmas strongly-nerved, minutely scabrous; sheaths smooth or scabrous, with united edges; leaf blades 2—5 mm. wide. Open woods and slopes, moist ground; 2000—3000 m. elevation. Midsummer—October.

Var. *laxa* Boyle has spreading panicle branches 4—9 cm. long; glumes sometimes purple. Western Texas (Chisos Mountains) to Arizona.

Figure 187

4a Rudiment placed obliquely at the end of the rachilla; tips of fertile florets at the same height. Fig. 188.

Melica mutica Walt.

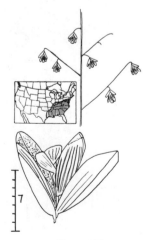

Perennial; tufted; plants 60—100 cm. tall; panicles 10—20 cm. long, with a few simple spreading branches bearing drooping spikelets. Sheaths hairy or scabrous; leaf blades 2—5 mm. wide. Spikelets fan-shaped, 7—10 mm. long, usually with 2 fertile florets and a bell-shaped rudiment, tilted sideways, at the end of the rachilla. This species, while seldom occurring in large stands, is the most widespread of the eastern *Melica* species. It grows in scattered stands in rocky woods. The name *Melica* refers to honey, but we do not know why Linnaeus applied it to this genus. April—June.

Figure 188

4b Rudiment placed straight on the end of the rachilla; tips of lower florets below that of the uppermost one. Fig. 189.

Melica nitens **(Scribn.) Hitch.**

Perennial; tufted; plants 50—120 cm. tall; leaf sheaths glabrous or scabrous; leaf blades 7—15 mm. wide; panicles 10—20 cm. long, with a few branches. The drooping spikelets are more slender than in the previous species and usually have 3 fertile florets. The rudiment is more slender and pointed than in *Melica mutica*. This species is probably more common than the previous one. The two are frequently confused but the position and shape of the rudiment should distinguish them. Scattered in rocky woods. Late April—June.

Figure 189

5a Lemmas without awns...6
5b Lemmas bearing awns. Fig. 190.

Melica smithii **(Porter) Vasey**

Slender tufted perennial; plants 60—120 cm. tall; sheaths downwardly scabrous; leaf blades soft, scabrous, 6—12 mm. wide. The panicles are very open, 12—25 cm. long, with slender spreading branches bearing spikelets at the tips. The spikelets are 18—20 mm. long, with 3—6 florets, and sometimes are purplish; awns are 3—5 mm. long. This slender woodland grass is found in moist forests. The occurrence in northern Michigan is the result of the cold post-glacial climate which once embraced that area. The plants resemble those of some of the perennial species of *Bromus,* from which they differ in the presence of the rudiment. July—August.

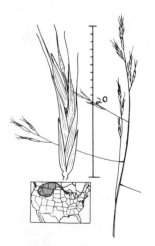

Figure 190

6a Culms with bulbs at the bases.....................................7
6b Culms without bulbs at the bases............................9
7a Lemmas acute or obtuse, glabrous............................8
7b Lemmas tapering to an acuminate tip, pubescent. Fig. 191.

Melica subulata (Griseb.) Scribn.

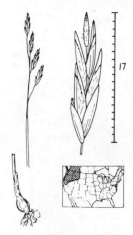

Perennial; tufted; plants 60—125 cm. tall; panicles narrow, 10—15 cm. long. The culms of this species and several following have small, onionlike bulbs, about 1 cm. long, at their bases, because of which they are sometimes called oniongrasses. Leaf blades usually 2—5 mm. wide. Moist forests. May—July.

Figure 191

8a First glume less than half as long as the spikelet; bulb attached to the crown of the plant by a thin stalk as much as 1 cm. long. Fig. 192.

ONIONGRASS   *Melica spectabilis* Scribn.

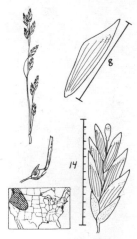

Perennial; plants 30—100 cm. tall; panicle slender, 10—15 cm. long. This is a handsome species with somewhat inflated spikelets, the lemmas purple-tipped. Leaf sheaths hairy; blades flat or rolled, 2—4 mm. wide. Gravelly mountain meadows and slopes. Forage value good. July—August.

Figure 192

8b First glume more than half as long as the spikelet; bulbs attached directly to a thick knotty crown. Fig. 193.

ONIONGRASS   *Melica bulbosa* Geyer

Perennial; plants 30—60 cm. tall; panicle narrow and stiff. Leaf sheaths and blades smooth or hairy; blades 2—4 mm. wide. This is perhaps the commonest western species in the genus. As the name implies, the plants usually have prominent bulbs at the bases of the culms. Woods and open slopes. Forage value good. July —August.

Melica fugax Boland. differs from the above species in having soft, thickish rachilla joints which turn tan and wrinkle when dried. The rachilla of *M. bulbosa* is thin, smooth, and white. Panicles 8—15 cm. long, with short spreading or drooping branches. Dry ground, Washington to northern California and Nevada. Good forage for livestock and wild grazing animals. May—June.

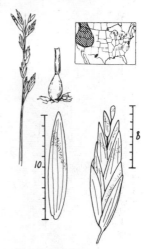

Figure 193

9a Spikelets with 3 or more fertile florets......go back to........8b
9b Spikelets with 1 or 2 fertile florets. Fig. 194.

Melica imperfecta Trin.

Perennial; tufted or with decumbent culms; plants 25—80 cm. tall, bearing spreading panicles, 5—30 cm. long, of numerous small, often purplish spikelets. In addition to the 1 or 2 fertile florets, there is a slender, yellowish rudiment which is 3—4 times as long as the very short rachilla joint which bears it. Gravelly soil. Good to excellent forage. April—May.

Melica torreyana Scribn. is similar but has hairy lemmas and a small rudimentary floret on a soft inflated rachilla half as long as the lemma. Central California.

Figure 194

52. SCHIZACHNE

Inflorescence a few-flowered panicle; spikelets disarticulating above the glumes; lemmas 7-nerved, awned between two teeth. Fig. 195.

Schizachne purpurascens (Torr.) Swallen

Perennial; tufted; 50—100 cm. tall; sheaths with united edges; leaf blades narrowed at the base, 1—5 mm. wide; panicles about 10 cm. long, drooping. The glumes of the spikelets are usually purple. This is a rather delicate grass of rocky woodlands. It grows in scattered clumps and is seldom numerous. Also found in Japan and Siberia. May—July.

Figure 195

53. GLYCERIA   MANNAGRASS

Tufted perennials of wet ground or water; leaf sheaths with united edges; spikelets in panicles, very fragile, disarticulating quickly above the glumes and between the florets; lemmas with 5—9 parallel nerves, usually blunt-tipped.

1a Spikelets linear, usually 1 cm. or more long, round in cross section, on short pedicels in narrow, erect panicles....................2

1b Spikelets ovate or oblong, flattened, 7 mm. or less long; panicles with drooping or erect branches..............................4

2a Lemmas obtuse; palea scarcely longer than the lemma.........3

114

2b Lemmas acute, the palea much longer than the lemma. Fig. 196.
Glyceria acutiflora Torr.

Perennial; rhizome-bearing; plants 50—100 cm. tall; panicles slender, 15—36 cm. long. Wet soil, swamps, or shallow water. The species of *Glyceria* all live in wet places, frequently in very shallow water. Their spikelets are very fragile and shatter at a touch when ripe. The plants are succulent and make good forage. May—August.

Figure 196

3a Lemmas 2.5—4 mm. long, glabrous between the scabrous nerves. Fig. 197.
Glyceria borealis (Nash) Batch.

Perennial; culms erect or decumbent; plants 60—100 cm. tall; panicles slender, erect, 20—40 cm. long; leaf blades 2—6 mm. wide; spikelets with 6—12 florets, 1—1.5 cm. long. The inflorescence of this species is similar to that of the next (Fig. 198). Shallow water and marshy shores. June—September. This and the next species are very similar. The seeds of their close relatives in Europe are harvested from the water surface for human food.

Figure 197

115

3b Lemmas 4—5.5 mm. long, minutely scabrous between the nerves. Fig. 198.

Glyceria septentrionalis Hitch.

Figure 198

Perennial; culms spongy, 1—1.5 m. tall, erect; panicles 20—40 cm. long, with ascending branches; leaf blades 10—20 cm. long, 4—8 mm. wide; foliage smooth or the leaf blades minutely scabrous; spikelets 1—2 cm. long, cylindrical, with 6—12 florets; lemmas about 4 mm. long. This is a tall, succulent grass of shallow water and wet places, probably yielding good forage. May —July.

Glyceria fluitans (L.) R. Br. resembles the above but has lemmas 5—6 mm. long, usually purple below the tip. Newfoundland to New York; South Dakota; Eurasia. In eastern Europe, the florets and grains of this species are harvested from the water surface for human food, being made into soup and gruel.

4a Panicle narrow, erect, the branches strongly ascending..........5

4b Panicle open, the branches drooping or spreading...............6

5a Lemmas about 3.5 mm. long; panicle dense, oblong, about 15 cm. or less long. Fig. 199.

Glyceria obtusa (Muhl.) Trin.

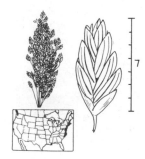

Figure 199

Perennial; culms erect or decumbent, 50—100 cm. tall; leaf blades flat or folded; 2—6 mm. wide; spikelets with 4—7 florets, 4—7 mm. long. *Glyceria obtusa* is a characteristic grass of the bogs of the Atlantic Coastal Plain, and found nowhere else. August—September.

5b Lemmas 2.0—2.7 mm. long; panicle slender, 15—36 cm. long. Fig. 200.

Glyceria melicaria **(Michx.) F. T. Hubb.**

Perennial; culms in small tufts, 60—100 cm. tall; leaf blades long and narrow, rough, 2—5 mm. wide; spikelets with 3—4 florets, about 4 mm. long. The slender, arching culms of this species fringe woodland streams and pools. July—August.

Figure 200

6a Spikelets oblong or ovate, mostly less than 2 mm. wide; lemmas thin, with conspicuous nerves....................................7

6b Spikelets broadly ovate, 2—5 mm. wide, with firm lemmas, the nerves not conspicuous. Fig. 201.

Glyceria canadensis **(Michx.) Trin.**

Perennial; tufted; plants 60—150 cm. tall; panicles 12—20 cm. long. *Glyceria canadensis* is one of the handsomest of grasses. The plump spikelets have a faint resemblance to snake rattles, hence the common name of "rattlesnake manna." Bogs, swamps, along streamlets. July—August.

Figure 201

117

7a First glume 1 mm. or less long...............................8

7b First glume 1.4 mm. or more long. Fig. 202.
> **Glyceria grandis S. Wats.**

Perennial; tufted; culms thick and tall, 1—1.5 m. high; leaf blades 6—12 mm. wide; spikelets 4—7 mm. long, with 4—7 florets; panicles 20—40 cm. long. This is a tall species, with large, dense panicles. It is one of the commonest species of the genus within its range. Marshes and stream banks. June—August.

Figure 202

8a Leaf blades 2—7 mm. wide, firm; culms usually 1 m. or less tall. Fig. 203.
> **Glyceria striata (Lam.) Hitch.**

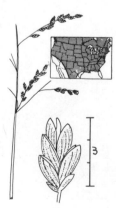

Perennial; forming large clumps; plants 30—100 cm. tall; foliage glabrous; leaf blades flat or folded; panicles drooping, pyramidal, 10—20 cm. long; spikelets 3—4 mm. long, usually with 3—7 florets, often purplish. The spikelets shatter very readily when ripe. This is the most common and widespread of the American species of Glyceria. Usually one will find a colony of it around every pond, runnel, or ditch, and it may also grow in moist woods. The plants provide good forage for domestic livestock and elk, especially in later summer when the growth sites are drier. Sea level to 3300 m. elevation. May—August.

Figure 203

8b Leaf blades 6—12 mm. wide, soft; culms usually 1—3 m. tall. Fig. 204.

Glyceria elata (Nash) Hitch.

Perennial; tufted; dark green; tall and stout, with spongy culms; panicles oblong, 15—30 cm. long, with spreading or drooping branches; foliage glabrous; leaf blades soft and thin; spikelets 4—6 mm. long, with 6—8 florets. This species looks like a larger version of the previous one, but it is restricted to the western states, where it is the most common and valuable forage species of the genus. Wet meadows, ponds, and moist woodlands. Eaten by all domestic livestock and elk; grazed primarily in late season when the herbage is less succulent and the habitats where it grows are less boggy. June—July.

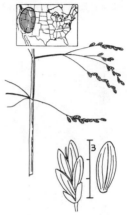

Figure 204

54. PLEUROPOGON

Inflorescence a raceme of a few large spikelets; disarticulation above the glumes and between the florets; lemmas with 7 parallel nerves, usually awned; paleas winged or awned; sheaths with united edges. Fig. 205.

SEMAPHORE GRASS

Pleuropogon californicus (Nees) Benth. ex Vasey

Tufted annual, 30—60 cm. tall; raceme with 5—11 erect or spreading spikelets up to 2.5 cm. long, each with 6—12 florets. Wet meadows and forests, northern coastal California. March—June.

Four similar species are found in the coastal region from central California to Washington.

Figure 205

119

Tribe 8. Diarrheneae

55. DIARRHENA

Rhizomatous perennial; culms in small tufts; inflorescence a simple panicle of few spikelets; spikelets several-flowered, disarticulating above the glumes and between the florets; lemmas stiff, 3-nerved; grain when ripe flask-shaped, protruding from the floret, thick-walled and rigid, the seed free from the wall. Fig. 206.

Diarrhena americana **Beauv.**

Perennial; producing numerous scaly rhizomes; culms up to 1 m. in height; leaves mostly low on the culm, the blades 1—2 cm. wide, scabrous or hairy; panicle slender, with short erect branches, nodding, 10—30 cm. long. Spikelets 10—18 mm. long. Growing in scattered clumps in rich woods. The peculiarly shaped grains are unique among our grasses. July—October.

Figure 206

Tribe 9. Brachyelytreae

56. BRACHYELYTRUM

Panicle slender, arching; spikelets few, disarticulating above the glumes; first glume obsolete, the second minute; rachilla extending beyond the palea of the floret as a slender bristle. Fig. 207.

Brachyelytrum erectum (Schreb.) Beauv.

Perennial; tufted; culms 60—100 cm. tall; leaf blades 10—15 mm. wide, flat, rather light green; leaf sheaths and blades usually hairy; panicles slender, 5—15 cm. long, with erect branches; first glume nearly absent; second glume up to 2 mm. long; floret cylindrical, firm, about 1 cm. long, with an awn 1—2 cm. long. Typical *B. erectum* is found mostly south of the glaciated areas of the eastern United States. The lemmas have stout, stiff hairs along the nerves and are otherwise glabrous. It grows in scattered stands in upland woods. June—July.

Var. *septentrionale* Babel grows mostly north of the glacial boundary, or southward in the mountains. The lemmas are sparsely and uniformly covered with minute appressed hairs or are nearly glabrous. Moist thickets and swampy woods. Also known from Japan.

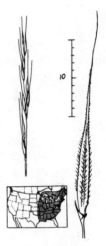

Figure 207

Tribe 10. Stipeae

57. STIPA

Tufted perennials; inflorescence a panicle; glumes about as long as the floret; disarticulation above the glumes; floret rigid, cylindrical, with a sharp hairy callus; lemma concealing the palea; awn strong, long, with a twisted basal segment. The sharp florets may injure livestock.

1a Lemma 5—12 mm. long, excluding the awn......................2

1b Lemma 15—25 mm. long. Fig. 208.
   PORCUPINE GRASS *Stipa spartea* Trin.

Figure 208

Perennial; culms in small hard tufts, about 1 m. tall. The panicle is erect or nodding, with few spikelets; glumes whitish; mature lemmas brown; awns 15—20 cm. long, with 1 or 2 sharp bends. The floret of *Stipa* species is a remarkable self-planting device. When it falls from the glumes, its sharp pointed callus readily penetrates the ground. The backward-pointing hairs prevent the floret from pulling out. The twisted portion of the awn coils and uncoils as the moisture content of the air changes, causing the bent arm of the awn to revolve slowly until it comes in contact with grass stems or other objects. Then the whole lemma is literally screwed down into the earth. Unfortunately the same process will occur if the florets get into wool or hair of animals, and these florets can thus cause serious puncture wounds on grazing animals, especially around the eyes, nose, and mouth. Prairies and dry open ground, mostly in the Midwest. June—July.

2a Lemma 8—12 mm. long; glumes 12—20 mm. long...............3

2b Lemma 5—6 mm. long, chocolate brown. Fig. 209.

Stipa viridula Trin.

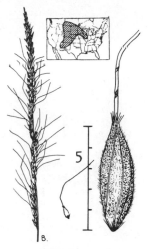

Perennial; culms 60—100 cm. tall, in dense clumps; panicles slender, dense, elongated, 10—20 cm. long The glumes are glossy and rather translucent. Awn 2—3 cm. long, with 2 bends. Dry plains. This species yields good forage. June— August.

Stipa robusta Scribn. (SLEEPY GRASS) is very similar, but taller (100—150 cm.). It has a narcotic effect on horses who graze it. Dry plains, Colorado to Texas and Arizona.

Figure 209

3a Lemma with a smooth whitish cylindrical summit; awn with 2 sharp bends. Fig. 210.

TEXAS NEEDLEGRASS   *Stipa leucotricha* Trin. & Rupr.

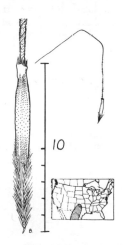

Perennial; culms 30—60 cm. tall; leaf blades 10—30 cm. long, very narrow, rolled, rough to the touch, dark green. The awn is 6—10 cm. long, with 2 bends. The lower sheaths contain very peculiar hidden spikelets (cleistogamous), lacking glumes and with a very short-awned lemma. This species begins growth very early, in late winter and early spring and is prized for winter feed. The awned florets may injure sheep. Dry plains. May—June.

Figure 210

3b Lemma without a whitish ring; awn with only 1 bend, the upper segment curly. Fig. 211.
NEEDLE AND THREAD   *Stipa comata* Trin. & Rupr.

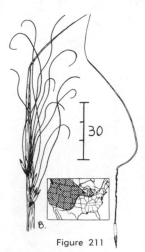

Perennial; culms in tufts, 30—60 cm. tall. The panicle is a mass of curly awns, 10—15 cm. long. The base of the panicle is usually partially hidden in the uppermost sheath. Needle and thread is a valuable forage grass in many parts of the West. It is grazed especially in the spring and fall, before the "needles" are formed and after they fall. Prairies, plains, and dry open mountain slopes. June—August.

Figure 211

58. ORYZOPSIS

Tufted perennials; inflorescence a panicle; glumes equal, as long as the lemma; floret hard, oval-cylindrical, the lemma enclosing and concealing the palea; callus short, hairy; awn weak, not twisted, readily falling from the lemma. This genus is similar to *Stipa* but differs in the weak awns and plump florets. Occasional hybrids between species of *Stipa* and *Oryzopsis hymenoides* are known.

1a Lemmas covered with short, appressed hairs or glabrous.........2
1b Lemmas covered with long, silky white hairs; panicle open, with spreading branches. Fig. 212.
INDIAN RICEGRASS   *Oryzopsis hymenoides* (R. & S.) Ricker

Perennial; culms 30—60 cm. tall, in dense, tough tufts. The panicles are very open, with scattered spikelets on the tips of slender, zigzag pedicels. The lemmas are brownish-black, but are covered with a dense cloud of white hairs. The awns readily break away from the lemmas, and may be missing from many of the spikelets. This is one of the most valuable forage grasses in the desert areas of the West. It is especially prized for winter feed. The large seeds are nutritious feed for livestock and formerly were used as food by the Zuñi Indians. April—August.

Figure 212

2a Spikelets (without the awns) 6—9 mm. long; leaf blades flat, all at the base of the plant. Fig. 213.

Oryzopsis asperifolia Michx.

Perennial; tufted, with numerous long flat basal

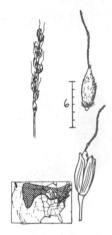

leaves; culms 20—70 cm. long, usually spreading, lacking leaf blades (sheaths present). The hard cylindrical lemmas are yellowish in color. Scattered in sandy or rocky woods. May—June.

Oryzopsis racemosa (Smith) Ricker is similar in general habit, but has long upper culm leaves and short basal leaves. The lemmas are black. Quebec to Delaware, westward to Kentucky and South Dakota. June—August.

Figure 213

2b Spikelets (without the awn) less than 3 mm. long; leaves thread-like; some leaf blades on the culms. Fig. 214.

Oryzopsis micrantha (Trin. & Rupr.) Thurb.

Perennial; in dense tufts; culms thin, 30—70 cm. tall; leaf blades flat or rolled, less than 2 mm. wide, scabrous; panicles 10—15 cm. long, with slender spreading branches, the spikelets borne near the tips; glumes thin and translucent; lemmas smooth or with appressed hairs, yellow or brownish; awns readily detachable, straight, 5—10 mm. long. Open woods and dry rocky slopes, intermediate elevations. The plants are said to have some forage value. June—July.

Oryzopsis miliacea (L.) Benth. (SMILO GRASS) has similar spikelets but broad, flat leaf blades, 8—10 mm. wide. It is cultivated for forage in California. Introduced from Europe.

Figure 214

59. PIPTOCHAETIUM

Inflorescence a panicle of a few spikelets; glumes equal, about as long as the rigid, oval-cylindrical floret; edges of the lemma not meeting, turned inward and fitting into a deep groove in the palea. Fig. 215.

PIÑON RICEGRASS *Piptochaetium fimbriatum* (H. B. K.) Hitch.

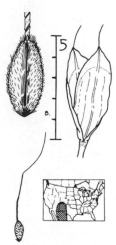

Perennial; culms in dense tufts, 40—80 cm. tall; leaf blades 1/3 to 1/2 as long as the culms, mostly at the base of the plant, thread-like and curved downward; panicles 5—15 cm. long; glumes about 5 mm. long, thin; floret dark-colored, glabrous or hairy; awns readily detachable, twice bent, 1—2 cm. long. Piñon ricegrass is said to be a valuable forage species. Open, rocky woods.

The genus *Piptochaetium* is one of the oldest known grass genera. Fossils of the florets have been collected from Miocene rock formations in the western states.

Figure 215

Tribe 11. Monermeae

60. PARAPHOLIS

Inflorescence a balanced cylindrical spike, the spikelets 1 at each node, fitting into a cavity which is closed off by the glumes; rachis disarticulating into single internodes when ripe, each segment containing a single-flowered spikelet. Fig. 216.

SICKLE GRASS   *Parapholis incurva* (L.) Hubb.

Low tufted annuals; clumps spreading; culms 10—20 cm. long; spikes curved, 7—10 cm. long, stiff. Dry banks and mud flats, salt marshes along the Atlantic and Pacific coasts. Introduced from Europe. April—August.

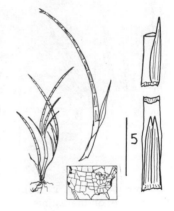

Figure 216

SUBFAMILY III. ARUNDINOIDEAE
Tribe 12. Arundineae
61. ARUNDO

Giant clump-forming grasses; panicles large, plumy; glumes slender, as long as the florets; disarticulation above the glumes and between the florets; lemmas 3-nerved, awned, covered with long hairs, giving the panicles a feathery appearance. Fig. 217.

GIANT REED *Arundo donax* L.

Figure 217

Perennial. This is one of the most spectacular of grasses of the temperate zone. The great culms reach a height of 6 m., and a thickness of 5 cm. or more. The plumelike panicles which are produced by well established clumps may reach a length of 60 cm. The stems do not persist over winter. Giant reed is a native of Europe, but is cultivated and naturalized in our southern states, and has proved hardy in cultivation as far north as central Iowa. The tough rind of the culms is used to make clarinet reeds. Fall.

62. PHRAGMITES

Tall rhizomatous marsh grasses, with plumy panicles; glumes shorter than the florets; lower florets longer than the upper ones; lemmas slender, awnless, 3-nerved, glabrous; disarticulation above the glumes and at the BASE of each rachilla internode; rachilla covered with long hairs, making the spikelets silky. Fig. 218.

REED *Phragmites communis* Trin.

Figure 218

Reed is a tall perennial grass, reaching 4 m. or more in height, with smooth, polished stems and long and very broad leaves. The plants spread widely by vigorous rhizomes, forming great colonies along the margins of streams and in marshes and ditches. In autumn the large panicles become very feathery because of the hairy rachillas. The lowermost floret of the spikelet is staminate or sterile. Reed is widespread in the United States and is also known from

128

all of the continents of the world. Fossil rhizomes of reed have been found in Europe, making it one of the few grasses known from past geological ages. July—October. Also called *P. australis.*

63. CORTADERIA

Giant clump-forming grasses with long, arching basal leaf blades; culms 2—7 m. tall; inflorescence a large, plume-like panicle; plants dioecious; female spikelets with lemmas covered with long silky hairs; male spikelets glabrous. Fig. 219.

PAMPAS GRASS   *Cortaderia selloana* (Schult.) A. & G.

The giant plants are often grown as ornamentals in the southern half of the United States. Old plants make large, circular clumps with drooping, fountainlike basal leaves, their edges bristly, sawlike. The silvery panicles may be as much as 1 m. long. They are often dyed and used in winter bouquets. Native of southern South America. Summer.

Figure 219

Tribe 13. Danthonieae

64. DANTHONIA   OATGRASS

Tufted perennials; spikelets few, in a panicle; glumes about as long as the spikelet, equal; florets usually 5 or more; lemma with a bent and twisted awn, arising between 2 teeth. The plants also produce hidden cleistogamous spikelets in the lower sheaths.

1a Lemmas glabrous except for the hairy edges and callus; plants of the western mountains. Fig. 220.

Danthonia californica Bolander

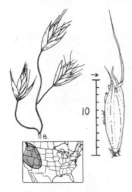

Perennial; tufted; culms 30—80 cm. tall, tending to break at the joints. The panicle is small, consisting of 2—5 large spikelets on spreading pedicels. In this and other species of *Danthonia*, the lower sheaths may be swollen and contain slender, much distorted cleistogamous spikelets called "cleistogenes." The culms break off just below the node where a cleistogene is present. Meadows and open woods. Of some value for forage. May —August.

Danthonia intermedia Vasey has the few spikelets borne in a dense, tuft-like panicle, 2—5 cm. long. Arctic North America, southward to Michigan and at high altitudes in western states. Grazed by livestock. July—September.

Figure 220

1b Lemmas hairy on the back as well as the edges; plants widespread in the United States. Fig. 221.
POVERTY OATGRASS   *Danthonia spicata* (L.) Beauv.

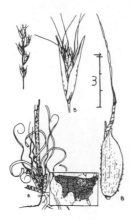

Perennial; tufted; culms usually 20—50 cm. tall. Most of the short, curly leaves are borne in a basal tuft. Their ligules are under 1 mm. long. Panicles short, 2—5 cm. long, with ascending branches. Poverty oats makes gray-green mats or sods on dry, sterile soils in the open or in thin woods. Forage value very low. Cleistogenes may be present, as in *D. californica*. May—September.

Danthonia compressa Austin has panicles with spreading branches. The ligules of the lower leaves are 2—5 mm. long. Open ground and in moist or dry woods, mostly in the Appalachian Mountains; Quebec to Georgia. June—July.

Figure 221

65. SCHISMUS

Small tufted annual grasses; spikelets disarticulating above the glumes and between the florets, or occasionally the whole spikelets falling with a stub of the pedicel attached; glumes and lemmas many-nerved; glumes nearly or quite as long as the entire spikelet; lemmas blunt or acute, with 2 short teeth at the tip, sometimes with a short awn between them; grain obovoid, golden, translucent, dropping from the floret. Fig. 222.

Schismus barbatus (L.) Thell.

Schismus grass is a winter annual weed in the southwestern deserts at low altitudes. Most of the leaves are basal. The plants are dwarf, 5—20 cm. tall, but furnish some winter forage. Lower florets about 1.8—2.2. mm. long. Introduced from the Mediterranean. March—May.

S. *arabicus* Nees is similar but has lemmas over 2.5 mm. long with acute teeth at the tip, sometimes with a minute awn between them. Arizona to California. Spring.

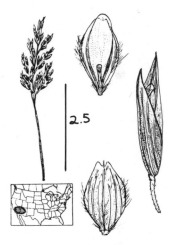

Figure 222

Tribe 14. Unioleae

66. UNIOLA

Perennials; inflorescence a panicle of strongly compressed and keeled spikelets; florets 3—many, the lower 1 or several sterile; disarticulation above the glumes and between the florets; nerves of the lemmas numerous, indistinct.

1a Spikelets with 4—5 empty lemmas; leaf blades thick and involute, less than 1 cm. wide. Fig. 223.

SEA OATS *Uniola paniculata* L.

Perennial; producing strong rhizomes; plants up to 1 m. tall; panicles dense, nodding, 20—40 cm. long. The very flat spikelets of the Uniolas are strikingly ornamental. Sea oats inhabits the coastal sand dunes along the Atlantic and Gulf of Mexico and the West Indies. The panicles are frequently harvested and used for winter bouquets and display-window ornaments. Spikelets may be found on the plants at most seasons of the year.

Figure 223

1b Spikelets with 1 empty lemma; leaf blades thin and flat, mostly 1—2 cm. wide. Fig. 224.

Uniola latifolia **Michx.**

Perennial; producing rhizomes; plants 1—1.4 m. tall; panicles open and drooping, 10—20 cm. long. While similar to sea oats, this is a woodland species of rich soil in the southeastern United States. It is highly ornamental and suitable for growing in shaded borders or wild gardens. Several other species of this genus with smaller spikelets also occur in the southeastern states. June—October.

Figure 224

Tribe 15. Aristideae

67. ARISTIDA   NEEDLEGRASS, WIREGRASS

Tufted annuals and perennials; inflorescence a panicle; spikelets 1-flowered, disarticulating above the glumes; floret hard, cylindrical, the lemma enwrapping the flower; callus sharp, hairy; awns 3, the lateral 2 often shorter than the central one, which may be coiled. There are about 40 species found in the United States. They are especially common on dry soil in the southern and western states. Most are indicators of overgrazing or soil disturbance. They yield little forage and are dangerous to livestock.

1a Central awn spirally coiled at the base........................2

1b Central awn not coiled..3

2a Glumes about equal in length; lateral awns about ¼ as long as the central one. Fig. 225.

Aristida dichotoma Michx.

Annual; tufted, in small, shallowly-rooted clumps; culms 20—40 cm. tall. The panicles are very slender, almost racemose. The species of *Aristida* are sometimes called wiregrasses or needlegrasses. They are typically grasses of depleted ranges or poor, sterile soils. This species is found on dry sandy or rocky open ground or in open sterile woods. Forage value negligible. August—October.

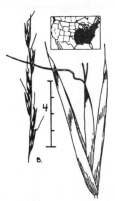

Figure 225

133

2b Glumes unequal, the first ½ to ¾ as long as the second. Fig. 226.

Aristida basiramea Engelm.

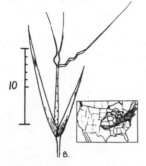

Figure 226

Annual; culms in small tufts, 30—50 cm. tall; leaf blades harsh, 1—2 mm. wide; panicles slender, racemelike, 5—10 cm. long, at the tips of the culms and in axils of the upper leaf sheaths. Dry sterile soil, open ground. August—October.

Var. *curtissii* (Gray) Shinners has very short lateral awns, 2—4 mm. long. Pennsylvania and Virginia to Wisconsin, Wyoming, Colorado and Arkansas.

3a Glumes about equal, 2—3 cm. long; lemma about 2 cm. long. Fig. 227.

Aristida oligantha Michx.

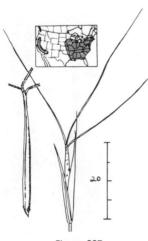

Figure 227

Annual; tufted; culms much branched, 30—50 cm. tall; leaf blades narrow, usually under 1 mm. wide; panicles 10—20 cm. long; glumes nearly equal, 2—3 cm. long, sometimes 3-cleft at the tip; awns 4—7 cm. long, spreading, about equal in length. The plants are wiry and almost leafless, most of the height being the bristly inflorescences. The sharp-pointed, 3-awned florets of this and other species of *Aristida* are great "crawlers." The pointed and backwardly-barbed callus penetrates hair or clothing easily, and every movement of the body of the host results in the floret digging in deeper, aided by the scabrous awns. Forage value negligible. Dry open ground. August—October.

3b Glumes unequal, the first about 1 cm. long, the second twice as
long; lemma 12—15 mm. long. Fig. 228.
   DOGTOWN GRASS   *Aristida longiseta* Steud.

Perennial; in large tufts; culms 20—
50 cm. tall; panicles narrow, standing
well above the leaves, appearing as a
feathery mass of long, reddish awns.
The awns may reach lengths of 6—8
cm. The narrow, stiff, straight leaves
may be mostly at the base of the plant.
Dogtown grass is an inferior forage species. The sharp awns and pointed callus cause the florets to pierce the facial
tissues of grazing animals, causing serious infections and sometimes blindness.
Dry plains and foothills, especially on
thin rocky soil or bare ground. July—
October.

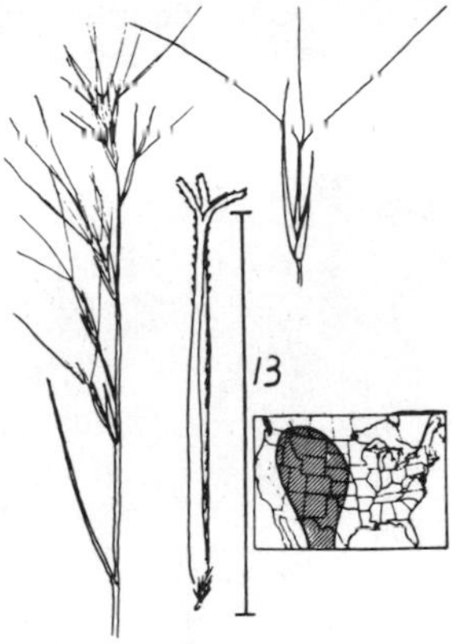

Figure 228

Aristida fendleriana Steud. is similar
in the panicle and spikelets, but most of
the leaves are crowded in dense, curly basal tufts. Widespread in
the Great Plains and western mountain states.

SUBFAMILY IV. ORYZOIDEAE

Tribe 16. Oryzeae

68. ORYZA   RICE

Cultivated aquatic annual; inflorescence a panicle; spikelets very flat, awned or awnless; glumes reduced to a minute cup; floret disarticulating above this, carrying with it 2 sterile lemmas about 1/3 as long as the fertile floret. Fig. 229.

RICE   *Oryza sativa* L.

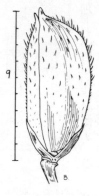

Annual; plants aquatic, stout, 1—2 m. tall; panicles drooping, the very flat spikelets hairy, awned or awnless. The structures which look like glumes are really sterile lemmas; the true glumes are the minute ridges which are left behind at the summit of the pedicel when the floret drops. Rice is one of the principal food crops of the world but its culture is restricted to moist or irrigated regions with warm temperate or tropical climates. In the United States, it is grown only in the lower Mississippi Basin and in Florida and California.

Figure 229

69. LEERSIA   CUT GRASS

Rhizomatous perennials; inflorescence a panicle; spikelets very flat, awnless; glumes reduced to a minute cup; floret disarticulating above this.

la Sheaths strongly downwardly scabrous; rhizomes slender, with exposed internodes; lower panicle branches whorled. Fig. 230.
   CUT GRASS   *Leersia oryzoides* (L.) **Sw.**

Perennial; culms up to 1.5 m. long, weak and often sprawling; rhizomes long and slender; leaf sheaths and margins of the blades armed with very sharp minute spines which can scratch severely. The plants are very rough to the touch and cling readily to clothing. The glumes of species of *Leersia* are the minute cuplike structures from which the floret drops. Cut grass often forms dense "jungles" along streams or around ponds or in marshes. July—October.

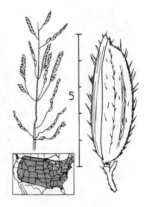

Leersia lenticularis Michx. (CATCHFLY GRASS) is similar, but has broadly oval spikelets, 3—4 mm. wide and 4—5 mm. long, arranged in neat overlapping rows.

Figure 230

Wet ground and swamps, Mississippi Valley and southeastern states.

lb Sheaths smooth or nearly so; rhizomes short and thick, densely covered with scales; lower panicle branches borne singly. Fig. 231.
   WHITE GRASS   *Leersia virginica* **Willd.**

Perennial; culms 50—120 cm. tall, weak and slender; panicle 10—20 cm. long, with a few simple branches, the spikelets lying closely parallel to them. Some of the smaller panicles may be hidden in the sheaths. Leaf blades yellowish-green. Damp woods and thickets; mud flats. July—October.

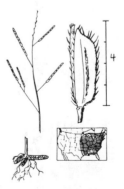

Figure 231

Tribe 17. Zizanieae

70. ZIZANIA WILD RICE

Tall aquatic annuals; pistillate spikelets all at the upper tip of the panicle, forming an erect brush, their awns several times as long as the lemma; staminate spikelets awnless, drooping, all on spreading lower branches of the panicle. Fig. 232.

WILD RICE   *Zizania aquatica* L.

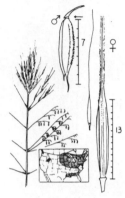

Annual; culms stout, 2—3 m. or more tall; panicles 30—50 cm. long, open and pyramidal. The spikelets consist of single florets, which disarticulate from minute cuplike structures which are the vestiges of glumes. Wild rice was an important food plant for the American Indians, who threshed the standing plants into canoes. It still furnishes some food for human beings and the grain can occasionally be purchased in stores. In nature, wild rice is an important producer of food for waterfowl. Shallow water, ditches, ponds, streams and marshes. July—September.

Figure 232

71. ZIZANIOPSIS SOUTHERN WILD RICE

Tall aquatic perennial; pistillate spikelets intermixed with the staminate ones on the same branches, awn-tipped; caryopsis oblong, free from the floret, with a short stiff persistent style. Fig. 233.

SOUTHERN WILD RICE   *Zizaniopsis miliacea* (Michx.) Doell.

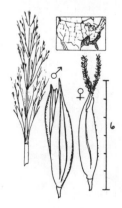

Perennial; plants 1—3 m. tall or taller, the culms arising from stout rhizomes; panicles nodding, 30—50 cm. long. Leaves very scabrous on the margins. The spikelets consist of single florets, which disarticulate from the vestigial glumes, as in the previous species. The staminate ones have 6 stamens instead of the usual 3. Marshes and along streams. May—June.

Figure 233

72. HYDROCHLOA

Immersed aquatics, only the upper leaves floating on the water; staminate and pistillate spikelets in separate small panicles. Fig. 234.

WATER GRASS   *Hydrochloa carolinensis* **Beauv.**

Perennial; culms slender, weak, up to 1 m. long, floating in water, the upper leaves on the surface. The staminate spikelets are borne at the tips of branches and the pistillate ones in the axils of leaves. Neither type has evident glumes, and both have only a single floret. Ponds and slow streams. Furnishes some feed for livestock. Blooming apparently rare. June—August.

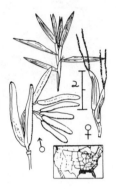

Figure 234

SUBFAMILY V. ERAGROSTOIDEAE

Tribe 18. Aeluropideae

73. DISTICHLIS   SALT GRASS

Tough rhizomatous dioecious perennials, growing in salty or alkaline habitats; panicle small, with few, crowded, spikelets; spikelets of staminate and pistillate plants similar; disarticulation above the glumes and between the 5—15 florets; nerves of the awnless lemmas numerous but faint. Fig. 235.

SALT GRASS   *Distichlis stricta* (Torr.) Rydb.

Perennial; spreading by stiff, scaly rhizomes; plants 10—40 cm. tall. The salt grasses are coarse, stiff plants of saline or alkali flats in the drier parts of the western states and in the coastal salt marshes. *D. stricta* is confined to the interior of the western United States. In desert areas, it is eaten readily by cattle, but it is seldom taken where more succulent forage is available. April—September.

Distichlis spicata (L.) Greene, a very similar species, grows in brackish marshes along our entire Atlantic, Gulf and Pacific coasts.

Figure 235

Tribe 19. Spartineae

74. SPARTINA

Perennials, usually with rhizomes; inflorescence a panicle of 1-sided spikes, the spikelets in 2 rows along the lower side of the rachis, crowded, very flat and keeled, 1-flowered, disarticulating below the unequal glumes.

1a Leaf blades flat when fresh, 4—25 mm. wide.................2

1b Leaf blades rolled, 2 mm. or less wide. Fig. 236.
   SALT MARSH GRASS   *Spartina patens* (Ait.) Muhl.

Perennial; spreading by slender, scaly rhizomes, forming large colonies in coastal salt marshes along the Atlantic and Gulf coasts. Culms up to 1 m. tall, usually shorter. This grass is tough and harsh, but is frequently harvested for hay, which is used as packing material. The plants are valuable as land-builders along the coast, trapping and holding the tidal mud. July—September.

Spartina gracilis Trin. (ALKALI CORD-GRASS) is similar, but is found on alkali or salty flats in the interior of the United States, from the Dakotas to Kansas, westward to Washington and California.

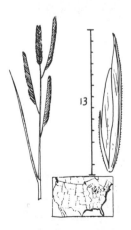

Figure 236

141

2a Leaf margins rough to the touch; plants widespread. Fig. 237.
SLOUGH GRASS   *Spartina pectinata* Link

Figure 237

Perennial; spreading by tough, scaly rhizomes which are up to 1 cm. thick; culms tall, 1—2 m. in height. The whole plant is coarse and tough, with saw-edged leaves. Slough grass was formerly one of the dominant grasses of the tall grass prairie region of the north central United States. Now it survives largely along roadsides, in ditches, and on wet ground. July—September.

Spartina cynosuroides (L.) Roth is taller, has numerous spikes; second glume without an awn. Salt marshes, Atlantic and Gulf coasts.

2b Leaf margins smooth; plants of Atlantic coastal salt marshes. Fig. 238.

Spartina alterniflora Loisel

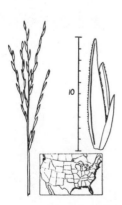

Figure 238

Perennial; spreading by rhizomes; culms .5—2.5 m. tall, thick and spongy; leaf blades flat, 5—15 mm. wide, tapering to a fine point; panicles narrow, the spikes slender and erect, 5—15 cm. long; spikelets about 1 cm. long, the floret smooth or slightly hairy. Coastal salt marshes, often growing in shallow water. Introduced along the coast of southwestern Washington. July—October.

Nearly a century ago, this species was introduced into southern England. There it formed a highly successful natural hybrid with a European species. This hybrid, *Spartina townsendii*, is now building extensive areas of dry land from former tidal mud flats there.

Tribe 20. Eragrosteae

75. ERAGROSTIS   LOVEGRASS

Annuals or perennials, usually tufted; inflorescence a panicle, sometimes with spikelike branches; spikelets small, with 3—many florets; glumes short; lemmas 3-nerved; disarticulation above the glumes and between the florets, or in many species the glumes and lemmas falling from a persistent rachilla.

1a Plants forming flat mats, the trailing culms rooting at the nodes...2

1b Plants erect or with somewhat decumbent culms, but never rooting at the nodes...3

2a Staminate and pistillate spikelets on separate plants; anthers about 1.5—2 mm. long; panicle dense. Fig. 239.

Eragrostis reptans (Michx.) **Nees**

Annual; stoloniferous; only a few cm. tall, forming delicate, bright green turf along streams and on wet ground. Spikelets borne in dense panicles, resembling clover heads. Lemmas very strongly keeled. While the two sexes are similar in appearance, they can be distinguished by the presence of anthers or stigmas protruding from the florets. Forage value low. Late summer and fall.

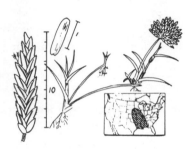

Figure 239

2b Spikelets all with perfect flowers; anthers minute, about 0.2 mm. long. Fig. 240.

Eragrostis hypnoides (Lam.) **B.S.P.**

Annual; stoloniferous, forming low mats. The panicle is usually open. Lemmas very strongly keeled. The anthers are minute and nearly round, with a bulk of less than 1/50 of the anthers of *E. reptans*. Like most of its relatives this plant is a warm-weather grass, growing rapidly from midsummer on. Stream banks and wet ground. Forage value low. July—September.

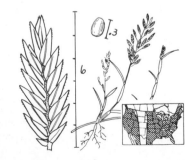

Figure 240

143

3a Lemmas when mature dropping from the persistent rachilla of the spikelet; (this can be detected by pulling lemmas outward and downward) paleas usually remaining on the rachilla. Fig. 241.
....15

3b Lemmas not falling separately; spikelets disarticulating between the florets when mature.......4

Figure 241

4a Paleas without long fringing hairs............................5

4b Paleas fringed with long straight hairs which nearly cover the spikelets. Fig. 242.

Eragrostis ciliaris (L.) R. Br.

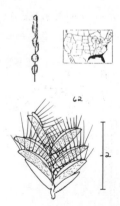

This delicate tufted annual grass grows 15—30 cm. tall, and bears dense cylindrical panicles, like those of the foxtail grasses, 3—10 cm. long. The tiny spikelets, only 2—4 mm. long, are immediately identifiable by the long, fringe-like cilia borne on the margins of the palea, which give a spider-web appearance to the spikelets. River banks and open ground. Widespread in warm regions of the world. June—August.

Figure 242

5a Spikelets 3—15 mm. long......................................6

5b Spikelets 2—3 mm. long; panicle elongated, dense, narrowly cylindrical. Fig. 243.

Eragrostis glomerata (Walt.) Dewey

Annual; tufted; plants 1 m. or less in height. *E. glomerata* produces a profusion of slender, cylindrical panicles up to 50 cm. long, with strongly ascending branches. The plants flower from near ground level to the very tip. The tiny spikelets have very thin, translucent lemmas. At maturity the grains are visible through the lemmas. Banks of streams and ditches, alluvial woods. July—November.

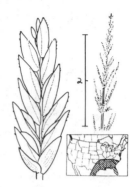

Figure 243

6a Spikelets sessile or nearly so, strongly keeled and flattened.......7

6b Spikelets on slender pedicels; lemmas keeled or rounded on the back 8

7a Spikelets few, distant along the few elongated panicle branches, a sessile spikelet and a cottony tuft of hairs in the axil of each panicle branch. Fig. 244.

Eragrostis sessilispica Buckl.

Perennial; tufted; plants usually 20—40 cm. tall. This is a tumbleweed grass, the panicle breaking off and rolling with the wind when mature. The leaves are clustered in a short basal tuft. The panicle may reach as much as 40 cm. in length. The main axis is somewhat spiral; the branches are straight, stiff, and bear sessile spikelets. Dry sandy plains. Forage value apparently low. May—June.

Figure 244

145

7b Spikelets numerous, in a dense panicle; no sessile spikelets and cottony tufts in the axils. Fig. 245.

Eragrostis oxylepis Torr.

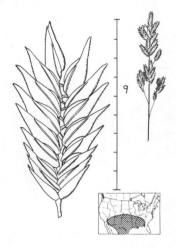

Perennial; wiry; tufted; plants 20—70 cm. tall; leaves 1—5 mm. wide, smooth except at the base of the blade. The spikelets are borne in 1 or more dense tufts along the axis or branches of the panicle. The spikelets often overlap like shingles. They usually have a reddish or bronzy color when ripe. Sandy or rocky open ground. Forage value apparently low. Also called *E. secundiflora*. July—October.

Eragrostis beyrichii J. G. Smith is similar, but the spikelets are pale instead of bronzy. Oklahoma to Mexico.

Figure 245

8a Panicle branches stiffly spreading; spikelets deep reddish-purple; lemmas strongly keeled. Fig. 246.
PURPLE LOVEGRASS   *Eragrostis spectabilis* (Pursh.) Steud.

Perennial; tufted; erect or rarely spreading, up to 60 cm. tall. Purple lovegrass has a large, open, dome-shaped panicle which makes up about 2/3 of the height of the plant. The axils of the panicle branches and throats of the sheaths bear conspicuous tufts of white hair. The leaf sheaths may be smooth or hairy. This is one of our most widespread grasses on sandy open ground, and one of the most attractive. July—September.

Figure 246

8b Panicle branches delicate, not stiffly spreading; lemmas not strongly keeled 9

146

9a Sheaths glabrous, or pubescent on only the upper edges........10

9b Sheaths pubescent along the edges, on the surface, and on the collar 11

10a Lemmas 1.8—2.4 mm. long; panicle broad, ovoid..............14

10b Lemmas 2.4 3.4 mm. long; spikelets 1 mm. or more long; panicle elongated, ellipsoid. Fig. 247.
SAND LOVEGRASS   *Eragrostis trichodes* (Nutt.) Wood

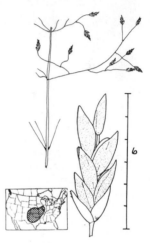

Perennial; tufted; 80—120 cm. tall. The open, cylindrical panicles may make up half the total height of the plant. The spikelets frequently have purplish florets and yellow glumes. Sandy plains and open woodlands. Sand lovegrass has high forage value, but has been virtually destroyed by overgrazing in many of the areas where it once abounded. August—September.

Eragrostis curvula (see Fig. 249) sometimes has smooth sheaths and might be keyed out here. It may be recognized by the lead-colored, short-pedicellate spikelets.

Figure 247

11a Sheaths and often blades bearing hairs, each of which arises from a little blister. Fig. 248.......12

11b Hairs of sheaths not arising from little blisters...13

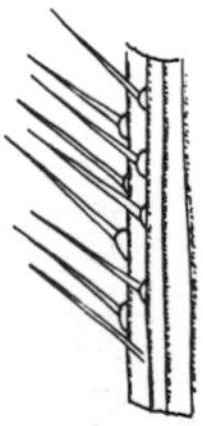

12a Spikelets 5—10 mm. long; lemmas 2.4—3.4 mm. long
........................go back to.............10b

Figure 248

12b Spikelets 2—5 mm. long; lemmas 2.0—2.4 mm. long............13

13a Panicle not over twice as long as wide; usually 15 cm. wide or wider 14

13b Panicle 3 times as long as wide; never over 12 cm. wide; cultivated and sometimes escaping. Fig. 249.

WEEPING LOVEGRASS   *Eragrostis curvula* (Schrad.) **Nees**

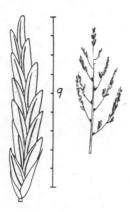

Figure 249

Perennial; tufted; 60—120 cm. tall, forming large round clumps. The leaves are long, drawn out to very fine drooping tips. The panicles are elongated and somewhat drooping; branches not bearing spikelets near the bases; spikelets dull straw colored or leaden gray. Native to South Africa, weeping love-grass was first brought to the United States as an ornamental, but is now widely planted in the southern states as a forage grass for revegetating abandoned or eroded crop land. It makes excellent pasturage and can be used for hay. The seeds are about 1 mm. long, smooth, amber colored except for the black-ish germ. Summer.

Eragrostis trichodes (see Fig. 247) sometimes has hairy sheaths and may key out here. It may be recognized by the long-pedicellate, usually bronzy or yellowish spikelets.

14a Lemmas 2.0—2.4 mm. long; larger leaf blades 5—10 mm. wide. Fig. 250.

Eragrostis hirsuta (Michx.) **Nees**

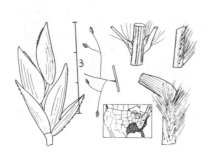

Figure 250

Perennial; tufted; plants becoming 1 m. or more tall; panicles large, open, cylindrical, half the height of the plant. The leaves are wider than in most other species of this genus and taper to long fine points. The summits of the leaf sheaths (see figure) vary from extremely hairy to glabrous. Dry soil, in open woods and fields. Summer.

148

14b Lemmas 1.8—2.2 mm. long; larger leaf blades 2—3 mm. wide. Fig. 251.

Eragrostis intermedia Hitch.

Perennial; tufted; reaching nearly 1 m. in height. This species has an open, dome-shaped panicle with slender delicate branchlets. The leaf blades are narrow, involute, and drawn out to slender tips; sheaths glabrous or the lower ones somewhat hairy. Dry sandy open ground. June—September.

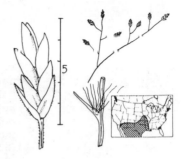

Figure 251

15a Plants perennial, usually 50—150 cm. tall, forming large clumps from hard, knotty bases; basal buds of next year's growth present at flowering time....................go back to................6

15b Plants annual, usually less than 50 cm. tall, from soft, shallow-rooted bases; no basal buds present at flowering time.........16

16a Spikelets with 2—4 (rarely 5) florets...........................17

16b Spikelets with 6—many florets (rarely 5 in starved plants)......18

17a Pedicels of *lateral* spikelets 3—many times as long as the spikelets; panicle large, diffuse, 2/3 or more of the total height of the plant; plants erect. Fig. 252.
LACEGRASS *Eragrostis capillaris* (L.) Nees

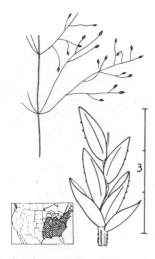

Lacegrass is a densely tufted annual, up to 50 cm. in height. Culms much branched at the base, the plants bearing numerous panicles; leaf sheaths somewhat hairy, especially at the throat; blades flat, hairy on the upper surface, 1—3 mm. wide; panicles open-cylindrical or elliptical, making up most of the height of the plants. Spikelets 2—3 mm. long, with 2—4 florets; glumes about 1 mm. long; lemmas about 1.5 mm. long. The minute grains are about 0.5 mm. long. Lacegrass is a common weed of open, dry situations on waste ground, in fields, and thin woods. August—September.

Figure 252

17b Pedicels of *lateral* spikelets short, rarely more than twice the length of the spikelets; panicles about half the length of the sprawling plants. Fig. 253.
Eragrostis frankii C. A. Mey.

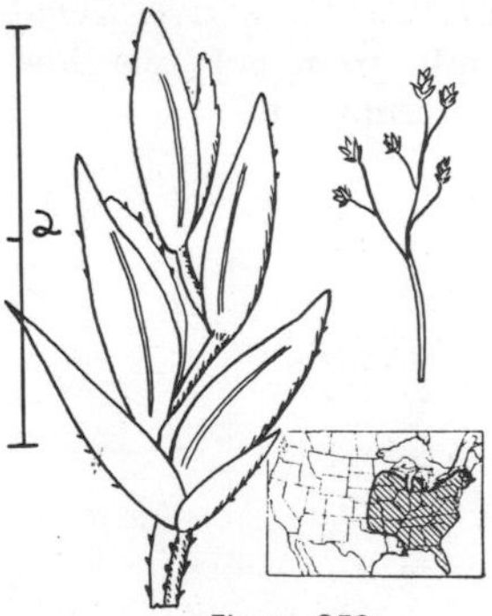

Annual; a weed of river banks and wet alluvial bottoms, *E. frankii* makes sprawling bushy tufts. The culms are seldom more than 25 cm. long. Leaf sheaths and blades usually smooth except at the throat. The ellipsoidal panicle is much denser than that of *E. capillaris*, because of the shorter pedicels. August—September.

Figure 253

18a Plants without glands on spikelets or branches; spikelets 2 mm. or less wide **19**

18b Plants bearing minute blisterlike glands on the keels of the glumes and lemmas and the branches of the panicle; spikelets 2.5—3.5 mm. wide when mature. Fig. 254.

STINKGRASS   *Eragrostis cilianensis* (All.) Link

Annual; tufted; culms erect or somewhat spreading; panicles ovoid or pyramidal, rather dense. The keels of the glumes and lemmas bear tiny circular glands. Stinkgrass is a vigorous weedy annual, with a strong, musty odor when fresh. It may be poisonous to horses if eaten in large quantities. Frequent in fields, gardens, and dry, disturbed soil. Introduced from Europe and now very common throughout the United States. Also known as *E. megastachya*. June—October.

A very similar species, *E. poaeoides* Beauv., has spikelets with glands on the keels of the lemmas also. The spikelets range from 1.3—2.0 mm. wide. It is less common than stinkgrass. Introduced from Europe.

Figure 254

19a Sheaths bearing a few long hairs on the margins at their summits; paleas remaining on the rachilla.............................20

19b Upper sheaths (and usually the lower ones as well) lacking long hairs at their summits; panicle rather dense, the lower branches usually single, bearing 11—40 spikelets; paleas falling from the rachilla with the lemmas. Fig. 255.

Eragrostis multicaulis Steud.

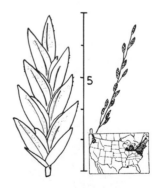

Weedy, tufted, annual, usually under 30 cm. tall. Spikelets 3—4 mm. long, usually with 4—8 florets. After the paleas fall, the minute zigzag rachillas remain as the only evidence of the spikelets. This species grows mostly as a weed in cities in the northeastern states. Although introduced in the Americas, its homeland is not known with certainty. Also known as *E. peregrina*. July—October.

Figure 255

20a Spikelets mostly lying closely appressed to the panicle branches. Fig. 256.

Eragrostis pectinacea (Michx.) Nees

Weedy annual; tufted; culms usually 20—30 cm. tall; plants branching freely from the base, forming dense, erect tufts. Spikelets 5—8 mm. long. The manner in which the spikelets lie parallel to the panicle branches is characteristic. Frequent on dry roadsides, waste ground, and cultivated fields; one of the commonest weedy annual grasses. July—October.

Figure 256

20b Spikelets when mature diverging strongly from the panicle branches; spikelets 0.7—1.4 mm. wide; lateral nerves of lemmas obscure. Fig. 257.

Eragrostis pilosa (L.) Beauv.

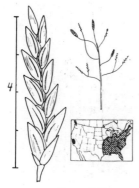

Annual; tufted; delicate; culms 10—50 cm. tall; panicles open, ellipsoidal. The tiny spikelets, 3—5 mm. long, stand away from the main panicle branches on hairlike pedicels. Leaf blades 1—3 mm. wide, flat. Introduced from Europe. July—September.

Figure 257

76. LEPTOCHLOA

Perennials and annuals; inflorescence a panicle of 1-sided racemes, the spikelets on very short pedicels, appressed in 2 rows to the lower sides of the branches; spikelets with several awned or awnless florets; lemmas 3-nerved; disarticulation above the glumes and between the florets.

1a Spikelets 5—10 mm. long; lemmas awned or awnless.............2
1b Spikelets 1—2 mm. long; lemmas awnless. Fig. 258.

    RED SPRANGLETOP   *Leptochloa filiformis* (Lam.) Beauv.

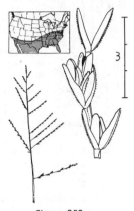

Annual; plants tufted, 20—70 cm. tall. The reddish or purple panicles may be half the height of the plants, with numerous thread-like spikes bearing the very tiny spikelets. Red sprangletop is a rather rampant weed, frequent on bottomlands, in fields, and in gardens. August—September.

Figure 258

2a Lemmas notched at the blunt apex, awnless, glabrous or nearly so. Fig. 259.

    GREEN SPRANGLETOP   *Leptochloa dubia* (H. B. K.) Nees

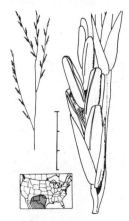

Perennial; tufted; culms 50—100 cm. long, tough, erect; leaf sheaths smooth; blades flat or somewhat rolled or folded, up to 10 mm. wide; panicles up to 15 cm. long, the spreading spikes 3—12 cm. long; spikelets 5—10 mm. long, usually with 5—8 or occasionally fewer florets; lemmas oblong, blunt, the tip notched, the midnerve sometimes protruding. The plants sometimes bear cleistogamous inflorescences hidden in the sheaths. This species has some value as a forage grass in the Southwest. Sandy or rocky open ground. March—September.

Figure 259

2b Lemmas tapering to a sharp point, awned, hairy on the nerves. Fig. 260.

Leptochloa fascicularis (Lam.) Gray

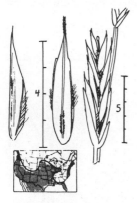

Annual; tufted; culms 30—100 cm. long, erect or horizontally spreading; plants becoming much-branched; leaf blades flat or somewhat rolled; panicles rather stiff, usually partly hidden in the leaf sheaths, 10—20 cm. long, the individual spikes up to 10 cm. long; spikelets 7—12 mm. long, with 6—12 florets; awns ranging from very short to 4—5 mm. long. Moist or alkaline soil, salt marshes, open ground. June—September. This is an unusually wide-ranging grass, extending southward through the American Tropics to Argentina. It is sometimes placed in the genus *Diplachne*.

Figure 260

77. ELEUSINE

Inflorescence of several radiating spikes; spikelets in 2 rows along the lower side of the rachis, disarticulating above the glumes and between the florets; florets several, flattened and keeled, the 3 nerves prominent, all close together. Fig. 261.

GOOSEGRASS　　　　　　　　　　　　*Eleusine indica* (L.) Gaertn.

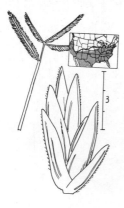

Annual; culms up to 50 cm. long, spreading horizontally or standing erect; plants often making flat mats. Goosegrass is a very common weed of fields, gardens, paths, and disturbed ground generally in the southeastern United States. Introduced from the warmer sections of the world. March—October.

Figure 261

78. DACTYLOCTENIUM

Inflorescence of several radiating spikes, the rachis extending beyond the spikelets; spikelets in 2 rows along the lower side of the rachis, flattened and keeled; second glume with a short, curved awn. Fig. 262.

Dactyloctenium aegyptium (L.) **Richt.**

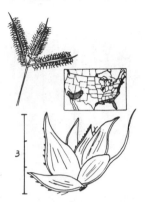

Annual; tufted; culms upright or spreading out and forming mats, rooting at the lower nodes. The seeds (ovary wall is lost) are brownish, about the size of a pinhead, and oddly sculptured. Weed on cultivated ground. This species was apparently once planted by the Indians along the lower Colorado River for grain. Introduced from Europe. Summer, or almost yearlong in the far South.

Figure 262

79. TRIDENS

Perennials; inflorescence an open or cylindrical panicle; leaf blades flat, not white-margined; spikelets with short or long glumes and several florets; lemmas split or toothed at the tip, with 3 prominent nerves, their tips often protruding as short points; disarticulation above the glumes and between the florets; stigmas purple.

1a Lemmas whitish, glabrous. Fig. 263.

Tridens albescens (Vasey) **Woot. and Stand.**

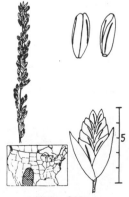

Perennial; tufted or rarely with rhizomes; culms 30—80 cm. tall; panicles spikelike; leaf blades elongated, 2—4 mm. wide, sometimes inrolled. This species may be confused with species of *Eragrostis,* but the fact that the lemma is split at the tip excludes it from that genus. The plants often grow in ravines and around water holes. They are succulent and make good forage, but are seldom found in dense stands. Also known as *Triodia albescens.* April—October.

Figure 263

1b Lemmas brownish or purple, hairy..............................2

2a Panicle open, with spreading, drooping branches. Fig. 264.
PURPLETOP   *Tridens flavus* (L.) Hitch.

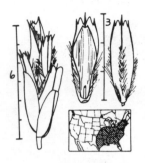

Perennial; tufted; culms 1—1.5 m. tall; panicles graceful and open, up to 35 cm. long; leaf blades smooth, flat, 3—10 mm. wide. The 3 nerves of the lemma protrude as little points. Open or partially shaded grassy places. Purpletop is eaten by livestock to some extent. It is attractive and colorful and might be grown as an ornamental. Also known as *Triodia flava*. August—October.

Figure 264

Tridens chapmani (Small) Chase is somewhat similar. It has a stiffer and more open panicle. A circle of hairs extends completely around the base of each main and secondary panicle branch. Dry woods, mostly on the Coastal Plain, New Jersey to Texas, north to Iowa.

2b Panicle slender and spikelike. Fig. 265.
                                    Tridens muticus (Torr.) Nash

Perennial; tufted; culms 30—50 cm. tall. The spikelets often have a faint purplish hue before drying. Leaf blades very narrow, about 1 mm. wide. Overgrazed lands and dry rocky slopes. Forage value low. Also known as *Triodia mutica*. June—October.

Tridens elongatus (Buckl.) Nash is very similar, but has leaf blades up to 3—4 mm. wide; plants 40—80 cm. tall; panicles 10—25 cm. long. Missouri to Texas and Arizona.

Figure 265

80. ERIONEURON

Low perennials with culms of 1 or 2 internodes; leaf blades with thick, white edges; panicles small and dense; lemmas long-hairy along the margins and the midrib; paleas long-hairy near the base.

1a **Plants spreading by stolons; panicles surrounded by a tuft of leaf blades; lemmas lobed at the tip. Fig. 266.**

FLUFFGRASS *Erioneuron pulchellum* (H. B.K.) Tateoka

Perennial; tufted at first, then spreading by short stolons; usually less than 15 cm. tall. The entire plant consists of a tuft of threadlike basal leaves, from which arise culms which have a single long internode and bear a cluster of spikelets and leaves at the summit. These culms soon bend over and root at the tip. This process may be repeated until a mat of the plant is built up. Fluffgrass is found on thin soils, overgrazed lands, and deserts. Forage value negligible; usually regarded as an indicator of overgrazing. Also known as *Tridens pulchellus* or *Triodia pulchella*. April—October.

Figure 266

1b **Plants tufted; panicles long-stalked, not surrounded by leaves; lemmas not lobed. Fig. 267.**

Erioneuron pilosum (Buckl.) Nash

Perennial; tufted; 10—30 cm. tall. Most of the very narrow white-margined leaves are at the base of the plants. The culm usually consists of a single internode. The plants are very shallow rooted and easily pulled up. Found frequently on thin rocky soils and overgrazed ranges of the Southwest. This species has little forage value and is generally regarded as an indicator of overgrazing. Also known as *Tridens pilosus* or *Triodia pilosa*. March—October.

Figure 267

157

81. TRIPLASIS

Panicles small, partly concealed in the uppermost sheath; spikelets several-flowered; lemmas blunt, 2-lobed, the 3 parallel nerves hairy, the central one protruding as a short awn; palea fringed with long hairs on its upper half. Fig. 268.

Triplasis purpurea (Walt.) Chapm.

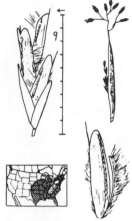

Annual; tufted; culms 30—75 cm. long, erect or spreading. In late season, the herbage may become quite reddish. The small terminal inflorescence usually protrudes somewhat from the uppermost sheath, but the axillary panicles are concealed in the swollen sheaths and have cleistogamous spikelets. Common on sandy lands. July—October.

Triplasis americana Beauv. is a similar species of the southeastern states. It is perennial and the lemmas have awns about as long as the body.

Figure 268

82. BLEPHARIDACHNE

Dwarf tufted perennial; inflorescence a dense panicle; glumes as long as the spikelet; disarticulation above the glumes, the florets falling as a group of 4, only the third one fertile; lemma with 3 nerves, all hairy and projecting as short awns; lemma split into 2 lobes along the midrib. Fib. 269.

Blepharidachne kingii (Wats.) Hack.

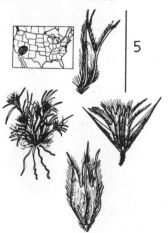

These diminutive desert plants are usually less than 10 cm. tall. They resemble *Erioneuron pulchellum*, but do not make stolons. Only the third floret contains a flower. Deserts from Utah to California. Spring.

Figure 269

83. REDFIELDIA

Rhizomatous sand-binding perennials; inflorescence an open panicle; glumes short; florets several; lemmas 3-nerved, with a tuft of long hairs on the callus; disarticulation above the glumes and between the florets. Fig. 270.

BLOWOUT GRASS   *Redfieldia flexuosa* (Thurb.) **Vasey**

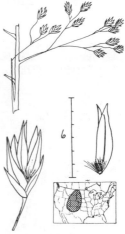

Perennial; culms 60—100 cm. tall; panicles large, pyramidal; leaf blades smooth and tough, elongated, inrolled. The spikelets when mature are fan-shaped, with conspicuous cottony tufts visible from the side. Because of the numerous long, slender rhizomes, blowout grass is able to keep pace with the shifting sands and eventually bind dunes into place. It is an important sand-binding grass on sandy plains from South Dakota to Oklahoma and Arizona. August—October.

Certain form of *Diarrhena americana* (see Fig. 206) may key out here. *Diarrhena* is a grass of rich, moist woods, with soft, flat leaf blades.

Figure 270

84. SCLEROPOGON

Dwarf stoloniferous perennial; dioecious; staminate inflorescence of awnless, non-disarticulating spikelets; pistillate spikelets disarticulating only above the glumes, the florets falling together. Fig. 271.

BURRO GRASS   *Scleropogon brevifolius* **Phil.**

Burro grass is a low perennial, 10—20 cm. tall, spreading by stolons and making patches. Staminate and pistillate inflorescences on the same or different plants. The inflorescences are small tufts of a few erect spikelets. Each pistillate spikelet has a number of florets, which are shed from the glumes as a unit, covered with numerous awns. Each lemma looks much like a floret of *Aristida*, with three long awns. The sharp awns and callus of the pistillate lemmas can penetrate hair, wool, and facial tissues of grazing animals. Burro grass tends to replace more desirable grasses on overgrazed lands of the arid Southwest. Forage value very low. June—September.

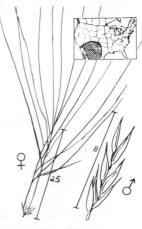

Figure 271

Tribe 21. Sporoboleae

85. MUHLENBERGIA

Tufted or rhizomatous grasses; inflorescence an open or spikelike panicle; spikelets small, 1-flowered, disarticulating above the glumes; glumes shorter than the floret or with awn-tips extending beyond it; floret soft; lemmas 3-nerved, awned or awnless, the callus usually hairy.

1a Glumes minute, less than 1/5 as long as the lemma. Fig. 272.
NIMBLE WILL   *Muhlenbergia schreberi* Gmel.

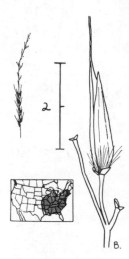

Perennial. The culms in early season are quite erect, but by flowering time they become much-branched and sprawl on the ground, the lower nodes often rooting. The erect portions of the culms are 10—30 cm. long. Leaf blades usually 2—4 mm. wide; foliage glabrous; panicles borne at the tips of the culms and from leaf axils, slender and weak, 5—15 cm. long. The glumes are vanishingly small, the first sometimes entirely lacking and the second only a few tenths of a millimeter long. Florets cylindrical, about 2 mm. long, hairy on the callus; awn 2—5 mm. long, very slender. Nimble Will may become a weed in shaded lawns and shrubby borders, but it does not seem very aggressive. It also is found growing in woods and thickets, roadsides and city streets, old fields, and meadows. August—October, rarely blooming in June or July.

Figure 272

1b Glumes at least half as long as the lemma.....................2

2a Plants producing elongated usually scaly rhizomes..............3

2b Plants lacking rhizomes (old tufts sometimes stooling out)........7

3a Panicles slender or spikelike, with short ascending branches; spikelets awned or awnless, on short pedicels.......................4

3b Panicles open, with spreading branches; tiny awnless spikelets on long slender pedicels. Fig. 273.
SCRATCHGRASS *Muhlenbergia asperifolia* **(N. & M.) Parodi.**

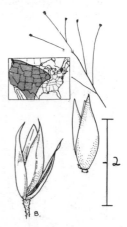

Perennial; bushy, 10—50 cm. tall, with rhizomes; panicles open, domelike, 5—15 cm. long; plants pale green in color; leaf blades 2—5 cm. long, 1—2 mm. wide; ligules minute. The grains are often swollen into spherical shape by the action of a fungus. Moist, often alkaline soil. June—September.

Muhlenbergia arenacea Buckl. is similar but has prominent ligules, 1—2 mm. long, Texas to Colorado and Mexico.

Figure 273

4a Leaf blades 3 mm. or more wide, more than 5 cm. long, flat and thin; lemmas awned or awnless...................................5

4b Leaf blades 1—2 mm. wide, less than 5 cm. long, usually rolled; lemmas awnless. Fig. 274.
MAT MUHLY *Muhlenbergia richardsonis* **(Trin.) Rydb.**

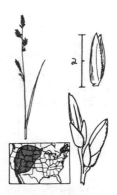

Perennial; much-branched, spreading by hard, thin rhizomes and forming mats, the erect portions of the culms 5—60 cm. long; panicle slender, 2—10 cm. long. Mat muhly is a grass of open, often wet or alkaline soil. While rather tough, it furnishes fairly good livestock feed. The densely matted plants furnish considerable erosion protection to the soil. Also known as *M. squarrosa* (Trin.) Rydb. July—September.

Figure 274

5a Glumes much longer than the awnless floret, tapering to awn-tips; panicle dense, spikelike, bristly. Fig. 275.

Muhlenbergia racemosa (Michx.) B.S.P.

Perennial; culms in bushy tufts, with numerous erect branches, plants 30—100 cm. tall; rhizomes densely covered with overlapping scales; internodes of the culms smooth and shiny. Anthers 0.5—1.0 mm. long. Prairies, dry or moist open ground; Mississippi Valley and westward, from southern Canada to the southwestern states. July—October.

M. glomerata (Willd.) Trin. is similar, but has large anthers 1—1.5 mm. long and dull, minutely hairy internodes. Marshes and wet soil; northeastern and north central states; transcontinental in southern Canada. July—October.

Figure 275

5b Glumes mostly shorter than the awned or awnless floret, lacking awn-tips; panicle slender....................................6

162

6a Culms much-branched, smooth and shining; axillary panicles produced at many nodes and mostly partly hidden in the sheaths.
Fig. 276.

Muhlenbergia frondosa (Poir.) Fern.

Perennial; rhizomes present; culms becoming elongated, 40—100 cm. or more long, the
plants becoming bushy and much-branched,
frequently scrambling through bushes or oth
er vegetation or sprawling; panicles at the
tips of the culms and protruding from nearly every leaf sheath, up to 10 cm. long,
rather dense; leaf blades flat, scabrous, 3—7
mm. wide; glumes 2—4 mm. long, tapering
gradually from base to an awned tip; lemmas 2—3 mm. long, awnless or awned. This
is a very common species in thickets and
woods and on roadsides and stream banks.
August—October.

Figure 276

Muhlenbergia bushii Pohl (*M. brachy-*
phylla Bush) is very similar, but has glumes
considerably shorter than the lemma; ligules very short, about 0.5—
0.7 mm. long. Mississippi Valley states.

6b Culms sparingly branched; panicles at the tip of the culm and of
elongated erect axillary branches; culms dull, the internodes usually covered with minute hairs, especially below the nodes. Fig.
277.

Muhlenbergia mexicana (L.) Trin.

Perennial; in tufts, producing abundant scaly
rhizomes; plants often becoming bushy; panicles
lobed; spikelets in dense clusters, the pedicels
very short; glumes 2—3 mm. long, tapering
gradually from the base to a short awn point,
about as long as the body of the lemma; floret
hairy near the base, about 3 mm. long. Awned
and awnless plants occur in the same colony.
Marshes, moist shores, open moist woodlands.
July—October.

Muhlenbergia sylvatica Torr. is similar but
has a more slender and open inflorescence, some
of the spikelets being on elongated pedicels.
The ligules are over 1 mm. long. Northeastern
United States and southern Canada, mostly east
of the Mississippi River. August—October.

Figure 277

7a Second glume not toothed.....................................8
7b Second glume 3-toothed near the tip. Fig. 278.
Muhlenbergia montana (Nutt.) Hitch.

Perennial; culms in large, dense tufts, 30 —60 cm. tall; panicles slender, with ascending branches. The 3-toothed second glume is the best identifying mark of this species. The old sheaths at the base of the plants become flat and stiff, like thin wooden splints. This species yields fairly palatable forage, especially when the herbage is young. Ponderosa pine, spruce, and fir forests, 2300—3300 m. elevation. July—October.

Figure 278

8a Panicle very narrow, the short branches bearing spikelets nearly to their bases..9
8b Panicle broad, open, the spikelets borne near the tips of the branches 10
9a Awn shorter than the lemma or lacking. Fig. 279.
Muhlenbergia cuspidata (Torr.) Rydb.

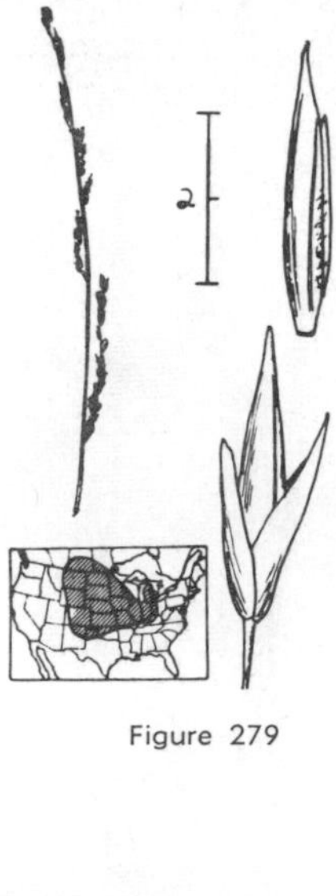

Perennial; tufted; culms slender and wiry, 20 —40 cm. tall; ligules minute; panicles very slender. Dry hills and prairies. July—September.

Muhlenbergia wrightii Vasey (SPIKE MUHLY) is similar but has a denser panicle, somewhat like timothy. The ligule is 1—2 mm. long. It is an important grazing grass on open or bushy ranges, ponderosa pine forests, from southern Colorado and Utah southward.

Figure 279

9b Awn 1—several times as long as the lemma. Fig. 280.
BULLGRASS *Muhlenbergia emersleyi* Vasey

Perennial; in large tufts; culms tall and stout, 50—100 cm. tall; sheaths glabrous, flattened and keeled; lower leaf blades up to 50 cm. long; blades flat or folded, rough, 1—4 mm. wide; ligules thin, 1—2 cm. long; panicles long and narrow, 20—40 cm. long, with ascending, overlapping branches; spikelets often somewhat purplish; glumes scabrous; lemmas hairy on the lower half, awnless or with an awn up to 25 mm. long attached below the apex. Some panicles may have both awned and awnless spikelets. Canyons and rocky woods. Said to be a good soil binder. September—October.

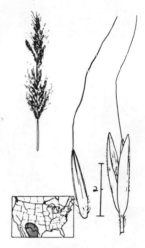

Figure 280

10a Plant forming sprawling, much-branched bushes from knotty crowns. Fig. 281.
BUSH MUHLY *Muhlenbergia porteri* Scribn.

Perennial; the much-branched plants will form bushy growth 1 m. in diameter and height if ungrazed. Because of the very high palatability of this species for grazing livestock, it is rarely seen except in the hearts of spiny bushes. The plants are semi-evergreen, the old culm bases producing new shoots in the succeeding year. Dry plains and deserts. July—September.

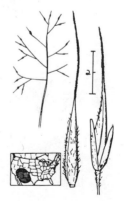

Figure 281

10b Stems erect, usually unbranched. Fig. 282.
   RINGGRASS   *Muhlenbergia torreyi* (Kunth) **Hitch.**

Perennial; plants forming circular or ring-shaped tufts, with numerous short, curly leaves, mostly clustered at the base of the plant. Ringgrass is a rather poor forage grass. Its presence usually indicates that better species have been killed out. Open plains, 1300—3300 m. elevation. July—August.

Figure 282

86. LYCURUS

Inflorescence a dense, spikelike panicle; spikelets single-flowered, in pairs which drop from the rachis as units; first glume with 2 or 3 awns; floret awned, hairy. Fig. 283.
   WOLFTAIL   *Lycurus phleoides* **H. B. K.**

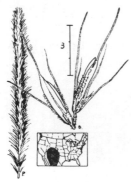

Perennial; tufted; culms 20—60 cm. tall. The dense, spikelike, bristly panicles are usually gray in color. The spikelets fall in pairs, one of each pair being on a longer stalk than the other. The lower spikelet is staminate and the upper one perfect. Open brushy hillsides and ponderosa pine forests, 1400—2600 m. elevation. A valuable forage grass, grazed especially in spring. July—September.

Figure 283

87. SPOROBOLUS   DROPSEED

Inflorescence an open or dense panicle; spikelets small, 1-flowered, the glumes usually shorter than the single floret; lemma awnless, 1-nerved; palea conspicuous; caryopsis when ripe readily slipping from the floret, its ovary wall becoming thick and gelatinous when wet (except in a few species).

1a Glumes plainly unequal in length...............................2

1b Glumes equal in length, nearly as long as the floret; plants annual, in small tufts with very shallow roots. Fig. 284.
Sporobolus vaginiflorus (Torr.) Wood

Annual; culms thin, wiry, 10—40 cm. tall, in small tufts; panicles mostly concealed within the upper leaf sheaths, or only the tips protruding. The lemmas are usually blackish-spotted, and the palea is often longer than the lemma. Both lemma and palea are covered sparsely with appressed hairs. Dry sterile open ground. August—October.

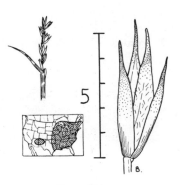

Figure 284

Sporobolus neglectus Nash is similar, but has shorter, plumper spikelets with glabrous lemmas. Northeastern and midwestern United States.

2a Spikelets 4—7 mm. long..3

2b Spikelets 1—2.5 mm. long.....................................4

3a Panicle open, with spreading branches. Fig. 285.
    PRAIRIE DROPSEED   *Sporobolus heterolepis* Gray

Perennial; plants forming large tufts; culms 30—70 cm. tall; panicles narrowly ovoid. The spikelets become much distended by the ripening grain, which is spherical and yellowish at maturity and about 2 mm. in diameter. The palea readily splits down the middle as the grain develops. Prairies. July—October.

Figure 285

3b Panicle spikelike, mostly hidden in the uppermost sheath. Fig. 286.
                                    Sporobolus asper (Michx.) Kunth

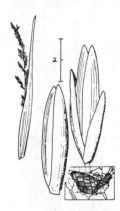

Perennial; tufted; culms 60—120 cm. tall; leaf blades flat or rolled, 1—4 mm. wide, tapering to a slender tip; panicles whitish or somewhat purplish in color, 5—15 cm. long. Open ground and prairies. August—September.

Sporobolus macer (Trin.) Hitch. is very similar, but has scaly rhizomes. Pine forests; Mississippi to Oklahoma and eastern Texas.

Sporobolus clandestinus (Biehler) Hitch. is similar, but has hairy florets; lemma and palea slender-pointed, the palea longer than the lemma. Dry sandy lands; Connecticut to Wisconsin, Kansas, Texas and Florida.

Figure 286

4a Sheaths glabrous or nearly so at the summit....................5

4b Sheaths bearing conspicuous tufts of white hairs at their summits. Fig. 287.

SAND DROPSEED *Sporobolus cryptandrus* (Torr.) Gray

Perennial; tufted, the erect or spreading culms 30—100 cm. long; panicles borne at the apex of the culms and in the axils of the upper sheaths. The tufts of straight silky hairs on the flanges at the summits of the sheaths are prominent. Sand dropseed is a rather important forage species on coarse or sandy soil in the West. It produces an abundance of fine, long-lived seed, and will recover rapidly from the effects of overgrazing. July—October.

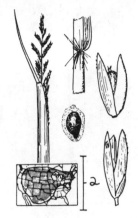

Sporobolus giganteus Nash (GIANT DROPSEED) resembles the above, but may be distinguished by its large size, from 1—2 m. tall, and slightly larger spikelets, 2.5—3 mm. long. Sand plains, western Oklahoma and Texas to Colorado and Arizona.

Figure 287

5a Panicle not more than twice as long as wide; leaf blades usually rolled. Fig. 288.

ALKALI SACATON *Sporobolus airoides* Torr.

Perennial; culms tough and rigid, in large clumps; plants 50—100 cm. tall. The large, open, dome-shaped panicles make up half or more of the height of the plant. The paleas of the florets often split as the grain develops. The plants can grow on very salty or alkaline soil. Although the herbage is tough, it is taken greedily by livestock, probably because of the large amount of salt in the tissues. Under a hand lens, minute salt crystals frequently can be seen glistening on the leaf surfaces. Plains and alkali flats, often on heavy clay soils. June—September.

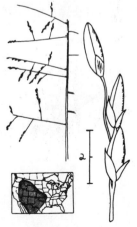

Figure 288

5b Panicle 3 or more times longer than wide; leaf blades usually flat. Fig. 289.

SACATON *Sporobolus wrightii* Munro

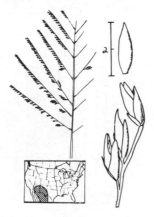

Perennial; culms in large tufts, stout and tough, 1—2.5 m. tall; panicles up to 60 cm. long, the branches bearing spikelets nearly to their bases. The plants furnish good grazing when young, and are sometimes cut for hay. River flats, especially where overflows occur. July—September.

Figure 289

88. HELEOCHLOA

Spikelets 1-flowered, flattened, disarticulating above the glumes; floret awnless; lemma 1-nerved; caryopsis wall swelling and gelatinizing when wet. Fig. 290.

Heleochloa schoenoides (L.) Host

Tufted spreading annual; culms 10—30 cm. long; panicles short and thick, the base hidden in the upper sheath; spikelets about 3 mm. long, flat. This is a minor weed of waste ground, railroad yards, etc. Northeastern and north central United States; California. Introduced from Europe.

Figure 290

89. BLEPHARONEURON

Inflorescence a panicle; spikelets small, 1-flowered, disarticulating above the glumes; lemma awnless, the 3 nerves hairy; palea hairy between the keels. Fig. 291.

PINE DROPSEED   *Blepharoneuron tricholepis* (Torr.) Nash

Perennial; tufted; culms slender, almost leafless, 20—60 cm. tall. The leaf blades are crowded in a basal tuft about 1/3 as long as the culms. The panicles are loosely cylindrical, somewhat grayish in color. This species is a good forage grass, especially in early season. Open parks and thin woods, ponderosa pine, spruce, and fir forests. July—October.

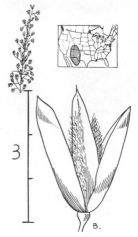

Figure 291

90. CALAMOVILFA

Rhizomatous perennial sandbinders; inflorescence a panicle; spikelets 1-flowered, disarticulating above the glumes; floret with a tuft of long straight hairs on the callus. This genus was formerly placed in the Agrostideae, but differs from other members of that group in numerous microscopic characters. Fig. 292.

SAND REEDGRASS   *Calamovilfa longifolia* (Hook.) Scribn.

Perennial; culms 50—180 cm. tall, in small tufts; plants producing long, tough, scaly rhizomes; panicles large, 15—35 cm. long; lemmas bearing copious tufts of straight white hairs on the callus. The plants are coarse and tough, but make considerable amounts of winter feed and are sometimes cut for hay. Sandy soil, hills and plains; shores of Lake Huron and Lake Michigan. August—September.

Calamovilfa gigantea (Nutt.) Scribn. & Merr. is similar but larger, and has hairs on the backs of the lemmas. Sand dunes of the Great Plains and southwestern states.

Figure 292

Tribe 22. Chlorideae

91. CHLORIS   FINGERGRASS

Tufted or stoloniferous grasses; inflorescence of several whorled, 1-sided spikes, the spikelets in 2 rows along the lower side of the rachis; fertile floret 1, with 1 or more dissimilar, sterile, often awned florets above it; disarticulation above the glumes.

1a Lemmas light colored, awned....................................2

1b Lemmas dark brown, nearly awnless; spikelets 2 mm. long. Fig. 293.

Chloris petraea **Swartz**

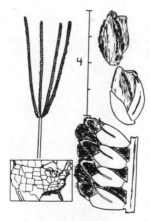

Figure 293

Perennial; tufted or with short stolons; plants up to 100 cm. tall; spikes 4—10 cm. long; lemmas chocolate brown; leaf sheaths and culms strongly keeled; leaf blades pale in color and with rounded tips. This species grows in the pine woods of the southern Atlantic and Gulf coastal plains. August—May.

2a Lemmas without tufts of white hairs near the apex.............3

2b Lemmas bearing tufts of long, whitish hairs on the edges near the apex. Fig. 294.

FEATHER FINGERGRASS *Chloris virgata* Swartz

Annual; tufted; culms erect or spreading, 40—100 cm. tall; some of the sheaths swollen; leaf blades 2—6 mm. wide; spikes 2—8 cm. long. The slender, vase-shaped panicles of spikes have a silky, white or pinkish cast because of the numerous long awns and fuzzy lemmas. The fertile lemma is about 3 mm. long. The rudimentary floret is wedge-shaped and bears an awn about the same length as that of the fertile lemma. This species is found as a weed in fields, along roadsides and railroad tracks in the Southwest. The occurrences in the eastern states are probably introductions. In New England the plants occur on wool waste heaps around woolen mills, the seeds being imported in the raw fleeces. July—September.

Figure 294

3a Plants 1—1.5 m. tall; leaf blades tapering to long, fine points. Fig. 295.

RHODES GRASS *Chloris gayana* Kunth

Perennial; spreading by leafy stolons; panicles vase-shaped, 5—10 cm. long; spikelets yellowish, each with 2 rudimentary florets above the fertile one. Rhodes grass is grown in the southern states for hay and grazing and is found growing wild in fields and on waste ground. It winterkills at 20 degrees F., and so is adapted only to the far South. Introduced from Africa.

Figure 295

3b Plants 20—50 cm. tall; leaf blades with blunt tips. Fig. 296.
WINDMILL GRASS   *Chloris verticillata* Nutt.

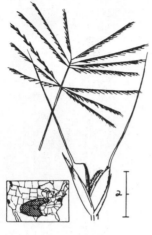

Perennial; culms tufted or with short stolons; leaf sheaths flattened and keeled; ligule membranous and ciliate, short; leaf blades grayish-green, 1—3 mm. wide; panicles of 2 or 3 whorls of stiff, widely-spreading spikes, each 5—15 cm. long. Spikelets rather widely spaced, the spikes slender; spikelets around 3 mm. long; awns 5—8 mm. long; fertile lemma hairy on the nerves; rudimentary lemma blunt. Windmill grass is primarily a plant of the plains of the Southwest, but may appear occasionally as a waif in the North. The mature panicles break off and roll as tumbleweeds. June—September.

Figure 296

92. GYMNOPOGON

Tufted perennials with short, blunt leaves; inflorescence a panicle of very slender 1-sided spikes, borne singly at the nodes of the rachis; spikelets in 2 rows on the lower side of the rachis, usually 1-flowered, the rachilla extending beyond the fertile floret and bearing an awned rudimentary floret. Fig. 297.

Gymnopogon ambiguus (Michx.) B. S. P.

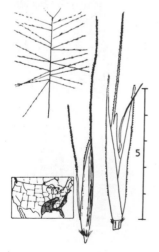

Perennial; tufted or with short rhizomes; culms 30—60 cm. tall, stiff and erect, with overlapping sheaths and short, broad, spreading leaf blades. The slender spikes may reach 15—20 cm. in length, and the whole panicle may be half the total height of the plant. Pine woods, mostly on the Atlantic and Gulf coastal plains. September—November, also in the spring.

Figure 297

174

93. CTENIUM

Tussock-forming perennials; culms tall, unbranched; inflorescence a single curved, 1-sided spike; spikelets densely crowded in 2 rows along the lower side of the rachis, disarticulating above the glumes; second glume bearing a protruding awn at the middle of the back; florets several, only the basal one fertile. Fig. 298.

TOOTHACHE GRASS   *Ctenium aromaticum* (Walt.) Wood

Perennial; tufted; plants 1—1.5 m. tall. The bases of the plants are surrounded by the coarse, fibrous remains of the old sheaths. Toothache grass is a plant of wet pine woods on the sandy coastal plain. The fresh roots are said to have a spicy smell. The plants furnish some forage for cattle in the South. May—July.

Figure 298

94. TRICHLORIS

Inflorescence a vase-shaped cluster of 1-sided spikes; spikelets in 2 rows along the lower side of the rachis; fertile floret 1, the second abortive, both bearing 3 long awns. Fig. 299.

Trichloris crinita (Lag.) Parodi

Perennial; tufted; plants 40—100 cm tall; leaf blades 2—4 mm. wide. The silvery panicle of spikes is vase-shaped, 5—15 cm. long, feathery because of the numerous long awns. Individual spikes are 5—10 cm. long. Spikelets disarticulating above the glumes; second floret rudimentary, reduced to awns; lemmas 3-nerved, all of the nerves extending into the awns, which are about 1 cm. long. The plants are sometimes cultivated for ornament. Fields and rocky open ground. Formerly known as *Trichloris mendocina* or *T. blanchardiana*. Autumn.

Figure 299

175

95. SCHEDONNARDUS

Dwarf tufted perennial; inflorescence skeletonlike, of solitary 1-sided slender spikes borne along a twisted rachis; spikelets borne in 2 rows along the lower sides of a triangular rachis, 1-flowered, disarticulating above the glumes. Fig. 300.

TUMBLEGRASS   *Schedonnardus paniculatus* (Nutt.) Trel.

Perennial; tufted; plants 20—40 cm. tall, with short, crowded basal leaves. Most of the height of the plant is made up of the skeletonlike panicle of very slender spikes. The main axis of the inflorescence is somewhat spiral. The whole panicle breaks from the plant when ripe and rolls with the wind, thereby distributing the seed. This is a grass of poor dry soil, especially on overgrazed or disturbed areas. Forage value very low. June—August.

Figure 300

96. CYNODON

Inflorescence a whorl of several 1-sided spikes; spikelets in 2 rows along the lower side of the rachis, 1-flowered, flattened, disarticulating above the glumes; lemma 3-nerved, awnless; rachilla extended behind the palea as a slender bristle. Fig. 301.

BERMUDA GRASS   *Cynodon dactylon* (L.) Pers.

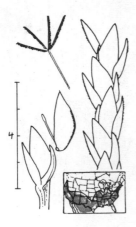

Perennial; producing both stolons and rhizomes and forming a fine green turf; erect portions of culms 10—40 cm. tall, bearing about 4—5 slender spikes at the apex. Bermuda grass is one of the principal lawn grasses in the South and furnishes much pasturage as well. It is very persistent when once established and may become a serious weed pest on agricultural lands. This species is apparently native to the tropics of the Old World, but has become widely dispersed in warmer parts of the world. Blooming period extends through the warm season, and may be yearlong in the subtropics.

Figure 301

97. BOUTELOUA   GRAMA GRASS

Perennials or annuals; tufted or with stolons or rhizomes; inflorescence of 1 to many 1-sided spikes, borne in a raceme along an unbranched axis; spikelets crowded in 2 rows along the lower side of the rachis; fertile floret 1, the rachilla bearing a second awned rudimentary floret; disarticulation above the glumes except in a few species in which the whole spikes drop. Important western grazing grasses.

1a Inflorescence of 1—10 spikes, which remain on the plant; florets dropping from the glumes..................................2

1b Inflorescence of numerous spikes, arranged in a slender raceme; entire spikes falling whole from the rachis when ripe. Fig. 302.
   SIDE-OATS GRAMA   *Bouteloua curtipendula* (Michx.) Torr.

Perennial; culms in tufts, arising from slender rhizomes. The plants range up to 80 cm. in height, most of the height being the long raceme of drooping spikes. Late in the season all of the spikes drop from the flattened rachis, which remains, bearing only the short stalks of the spikes. Side-oats is a very attractive grass, with brilliant orange anthers, contrasting with the usually purple spikes. The name "side-oats" refers to the fact that most of the spikes droop toward one side of the rachis. This is one of the most valuable forage grasses in the western states, furnishing good feed yearlong. Dry plains and open rocky hillsides, from near sea level to 2700 m. June—September.

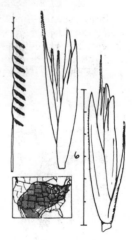

Figure 302

2a Plants erect or spreading; internodes of the culms not woolly.....3

2b Plant producing elongate stolons, the internodes covered with conspicuous short white wool. Fig. 303.

BLACK GRAMA   *Bouteloua eriopoda* Torr.

Figure 303

Perennial; plants sprawling, making bushy clumps, the stems thin and weak, rooting at the nodes. The 2—8 spikes are more slender than in the other species of this genus. Black grama is one of the best forage grasses in the southwestern states, furnishing good feed yearlong. Because of its ability to spread by stolons, it stands grazing well and recovers quickly from overuse. Open dry plains and hills, 670—1800 m. elevation. July—September.

3a Rachis of the spike bearing spikelets to the tip; keels of glumes usually not black-dotted...4

3b Rachis of the spike extending beyond the spikelets as a naked point 5—8 mm. long; keel of the second glume bearing prominent black dots. Fig. 304.

HAIRY GRAMA   *Bouteloua hirsuta* Lag.

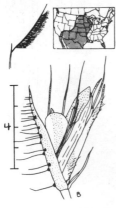

Figure 304

Perennial; tufted; culms 20—60 cm. tall; leaves short, curly, mostly at the base of the plants. Hairy grama is a highly prized forage grass widespread west of the Mississippi, especially on dry plains and hills, from 670—1800 m. elevation. In the Middle West it is usually found on dry hilltops. Hairy grama furnishes good feed yearlong, but is especially valued for wintertime use. July—October.

4a Spikes 3—7 per culm, each 1—2 cm. long; keels of glumes without long hairs; shallow-rooted annual plants with soft bases. Fig. 305. SIX-WEEKS GRAMA *Bouteloua barbata* Lag.

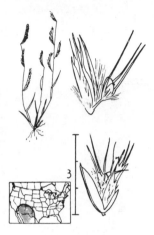

Annual; culms 10—30 cm. long, in small tufts, erect or more commonly spreading out and forming flat mats. The seeds germinate after rains, and the plants mature and die rapidly, hence the name "six-weeks grama." The six-weeks grasses, belonging to a number of genera, furnish short-season feed after heavy rains, but their total forage production is small and they are highly undependable as forage plants. Dry plains, especially on overgrazed pastures. July—October.

Figure 305

4b Spikes 1—3 per culm, each 2.5—5 cm. long; keels of second glumes bearing scattered long hairs; perennial, with hard bases. Fig. 306. BLUE GRAMA *Bouteloua gracilis* (H. B. K.) Lag.

Perennial; tufted; culms 20—100 cm. tall; most of the curly leaves are at the base of the plant. Blue grama is an excellent forage grass on the Great Plains and in the western mountains, furnishing good feed both summer and winter. Open plains, open or lightly timbered mountainsides. It may be confused with buffalo grass (Fig. 307), with which it often grows, but blue grama lacks the creeping stolons of buffalo grass. June—October.

Figure 306

98. BUCHLOË

Low creeping perennial; plants unisexual; pistillate spikelets enclosed in yellow, bony beadlike structures borne in leaf axils; staminate spikelets borne on 1—3 1-sided spikes. Fig. 307.

BUFFALO GRASS *Buchloë dactyloides* **Englem.**

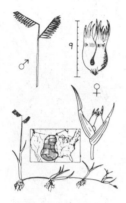

Figure 307

Perennial; spreading widely by stolons; pistillate spikelets enclosed in beadlike bodies with a short green crown on top; staminate spikelets in short, flaglike spikes. The two sexes are borne on separate plants. The diminutive plants are rarely more than 20 cm. tall. Leaves short, curly, grayish-green. Despite its small size, this species is one of the most important forage grasses of the Great Plains, furnishing excellent forage yearlong. It closely resembles *Hilaria belangeri* (see Fig. 309). For ways of distinguishing the two when not fruiting, see the discussion under that species. Buffalo grass frequently grows with blue grama grass (see *Bouteloua gracilis*, Fig. 306) and resembles it, except that the grama grass lacks stolons. Blooming time mostly in the spring, but also later in the season.

99. MUNROA

Low tufted sprawling annual; leaves short and stiff; inflorescences of reduced 1-sided spikes of a few spikelets, concealed within the sheaths of the upper leaves; florets several; lemmas 3-nerved, with a short, stiff awn; disarticulation above the glumes. Fig. 308.

FALSE BUFFALO GRASS *Munroa squarrosa* **(Nutt.) Torr.**

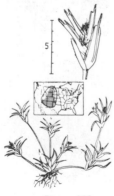

Leaves of *Munroa* are stiff, harsh, and somewhat curled backwards. The spikelets are borne in 2's or 3's on short 1-sided spikes. The small vegetative leaves and glumes are similar and hard to distinguish. The plants grow on overgrazed or disturbed soil in blowouts, around prairie dog towns, corrals, etc. Forage value very low. June—August.

Figure 308

100. HILARIA

Rhizomatous or stoloniferous perennials of warm, dry climates; inflorescence a balanced spike; spikelets in groups of 3, which drop from the thin rachis as a group; lateral 2 spikelets 2-flowered, staminate; central spikelet of each group with 1 perfect flower.

1α **Plants spreading by slender creeping stolons; culms 10—30 cm. tall. Fig. 309.**
  CURLY MESQUITE GRASS   *Hilaria belangeri* (Steud.) Nash

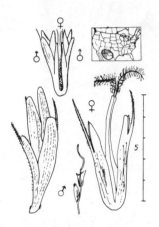

Figure 309

Perennial; forming extensive flat mats, the stolons rooting at the nodes. Dry plains, foothills, and brushy land, 650—1800 m. elevation; often on heavy clay soils. Blooming occurs sporadically during the growing season.

Curly mesquite is an important range grass in the Southwest. Because of its stolons, it stands up well under heavy grazing. Where it occurs with buffalo grass, it is regarded as inferior to buffalo, being less productive and not curing as well. The plants greatly resemble those of buffalo grass (*Buchloë dactyloides*, see Fig. 307), but may be distinguished by the spikelets and by the following features: 1. Color. Curly mesquite is light green when fresh, whitish when dry. Buffalo grass is grayish or olive green when fresh; tan, brownish or purplish when dry. 2. Stolons. The stolons of curly mesquite are round in cross section, very slender, and have tufts of hair at the joints. . Those of buffalo grass are oval in cross section, stouter, and smooth at the joints.

1b Plants erect, without stolons; rhizomes present. Fig. 310.
   GALLETA GRASS *Hilaria jamesii* (Torr.) Benth.

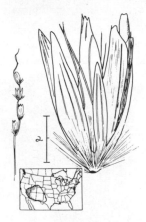

Figure 310

Perennial; culms tough, erect, 30—50 cm. tall, from stout, scaly rhizomes. The racemes of clustered spikelets are whitish. After the groups of spikelets fall, the rachis remains behind as a thin, zigzag straw. Galleta (pronounced gieyetta) is an important forage grass on dry plains and deserts in the Southwest. It is fairly palatable to horses and cattle when fresh and green, but is scarcely eaten when dry. June—August.

Hilaria mutica Benth. (TOBOSA GRASS) is very similar, but the first glume on each lateral spikelet is fan-shaped. Heavy clay soils, especially on river bottoms where flooding occurs. Western Texas to Arizona. *Hilaria rigida* (Thurb.) Benth. (BIG GALLETA) is larger, and has the culms covered with a dense white felt of hairs. Southwestern deserts.

Tribe 23. Pappophoreae

101. COTTEA

Perennial, with hard knotty crowns; spikelets in panicles, disarticulating above the glumes and between the florets; lemmas parallel-veined, their tips much lobed; nerves protruding as awns. Fig. 311.

Cottea pappophoroides Kunth

Foliage hairy; culms to 65 cm. tall; panicles narrow, 10—18 cm. long; spikelets bristly because of the many awns; marginal nerves of the lemmas separate nearly to the base; callus and lower margins of the lemmas copiously ciliate; palea ciliate on the lower margins; spikelets 7—9 mm. long. Dry sandy slopes in canyons, between 2—3000 ft. elevation; western Texas, Arizona, and Mexico. September and October.

Figure 311

102. PAPPOPHORUM

Tufted perennials; inflorescence a spikelike panicle; spikelets with 4—6 florets, but only the 1—3 lower ones fertile; disarticulation above the glumes; glumes equal, nearly as long as the entire spikelet; lemmas many-nerved, each nerve extending into an awn. Fig. 312.

PAPPUS GRASS   *Pappophorum bicolor* Fourn.

Erect, up to 80 cm. tall; panicles straight and stiff, 10—20 cm. long; bristly because of the many awns of the pinkish spikelets. Southwestern plains and deserts. May and June.

P. mucronulatum Nees is similar but the spikelets lack pinkish coloration. Southern Texas to Arizona. May and June.

Figure 312

103. ENNEAPOGON

Panicles gray, narrow and elongated; glumes as long as the spikelet; florets 3, only the basal one fertile, falling together; lemma many-nerved, with 9 awns, which are feathery-hairy on the lower half. Fig. 313.

PAPPUS GRASS   *Enneapogon desvauxii* Beauv.

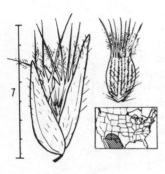

Perennial; tufted; culms 20—40 cm. long; panicles spikelike. Leaf blades threadlike, about 1 mm. wide. The lower sheaths are somewhat swollen, and contain cleistogamous spikelets which have nearly awnless lemmas. Several related species in the genus *Pappophorum* lack the feathery hairs on the awns. Dry desert hills and plains, from western Texas to Arizona and southward. Forage value low. Also called *Pappophorum wrightii*. September—October.

Figure 313

104. ORCUTTIA

Dwarf annuals; in dense tufts; inflorescence a short dense spike of a few erect spikelets which remain on the rachis after maturity; glumes shorter than the florets, the first narrowly lanceolate, the second usually 3-lobed; lemmas with many conspicuous parallel nerves, several extending into each of about 5—7 teeth at the broad apex; lower florets apparently staminate or sterile, the upper containing caryopses. Fig. 314.

Orcuttia greenei Vasey

This small genus consists of 4 species native to drying pools and mud flats from Baja California to Shasta County, mostly in interior California. None is common. Spring.

Figure 314

Tribe 24. Zoiseae

105. ZOISIA

Rhizomatous perennial; inflorescence a slender raceme; spikelets 1-flowered; first glume absent; second glume folded and keeled, the lower edges united, stiff; lemma hidden inside the glume. Fig. 315.

ZOYSIA GRASS; MEYER ZOYSIA   *Zoisia matrella* (L.) Merr.,
Var. japonica (Hack.) Forbes

Leafy perennial; low; having many wiry rhizomes and forming a dense turf. The spikelets lack lodicules and do not open up. The elongated slender style branches emerge through the tip of the spikelet, followed later by the anthers. The glume has a split tip and a short awn.

This species is often grown for lawns in the southern states. It makes a good lawn, but turns brown and dormant early. Apparently it seldom produces flowers, and is usually planted by "plugs," or small bits of turf. In the vegetative condition it may be recognized by its rather harsh, fine-tipped leaves and the thin, hard rhizomes.

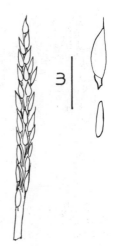

Figure 315

106. TRAGUS

Tufted annual; spikelets borne in spiny clusters along an unbranched rachis; glumes covered with hooked prickles. Fig. 316.

COCKLEBUR GRASS   *Tragus berteronianus* Schult.

Annual; culms 10—40 cm. long, spreading. The burs are borne along a slender raceme, from which they fall readily. Each bur consists of a group of 2—5 spikelets, but the second glumes of the 2 lower spikelets are covered with hooked prickles and conceal the remainder. The plants occur on dry open ground in the Southwest and also at scattered points on the East Coast where wool is processed. The burs are readily transported by the wool of sheep. Probably introduced from the Old World; extending through the warmer portions of both hemispheres. August—October.

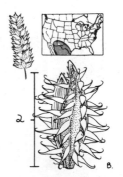

Figure 316

SUBFAMILY VI. PANICOIDEAE
Tribe 25. Paniceae
107. MELINIS

Sprawling perennials; inflorescence a many-flowered panicle; spikelets disarticulating below the glumes; first glume minute, second glume and sterile lemma equal, concealing the floret; fertile floret 1, with a long awn. Fig. 317.

MOLASSES GRASS   *Melinis minutiflora* Beauv.

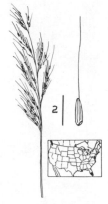

Molasses grass has a peculiar sweet odor. The foliage is covered with sticky hairs, a unique situation not found elsewhere among the grasses.

The minute spikelets are strongly nerved. While of tropical African origin, the species is widely planted as a forage grass in the Americas and has been introduced into southern Florida. In Brazil it is reputed to repel mosquitoes because of the odor.

Figure 317

108. PANICUM   PANICUM

Tufted or rhizomatous grasses; annuals or perennials; inflorescence a panicle, the branches sometimes racemelike; spikelets dorsally compressed; first glume short; second glume and sterile lemma equal, papery, concealing the shorter rigid fertile floret, which is shiny, awnless, and with inrolled edges which cover the edges of the flat palea.

1a Plants blooming twice, bearing panicles at the tips of the culms in spring or early summer, and small axillary panicles later; winter rosettes of short, broad leaves present in most species; all perennial species. Fig. 318......2

1b Plants blooming once, all the panicles produced at the same period; winter rosettes not present; plants annual or perennial.........11

Figure 318

2a Leaf blades of the culms less than 15 times longer than wide; plants forming winter rosettes of short, broad leaves....................3

2b Leaf blades of the culms very narrow, 20 or more times longer than wide; plants without winter rosettes of broad leaves. Fig. 319.

Panicum depauperatum **Muhl.**

Perennial; tufted; plants 15—40 cm tall, with hairy or smooth leaf blades, up to 15 cm. long and 2—5 mm. wide. The terminal panicles produced in May and June, are open, pyramid-shaped, and on long, slender peduncles. The secondary panicles consist of a few spikelets and are concealed among the basal leaf blades. The second glume and sterile lemma form an empty beak which protrudes beyond the tip of the fertile lemma. Open dry woods and barren ground. May—June.

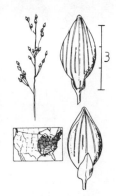

Figure 319

3a Ligules conspicuous, of straight hairs, 2—5 mm. long............4

3b Ligules 1 mm. or less long......................................5

4a Upper leaf sheaths glabrous; lower sheaths also usually glabrous; leaf blades glabrous or sometimes hairy on the edges only. Fig. 320.

Panicum lindheimeri **Nash**

Perennial; tufted, at first rather slender, 30—100 cm. tall. The plants later produce dense tufts of short, leafy branches, in the axils of the leaves, with small secondary panicles partially concealed among these leaves. The culms may then topple and the plants form flat circular mats. Open dry ground and dry open woods. Terminal panicles blooming from May—July.

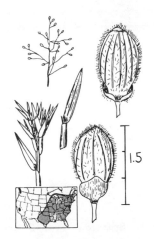

Figure 320

4b Leaf sheaths and usually the blades conspicuously hairy. Fig. 321.
Panicum lanuginosum Ell.

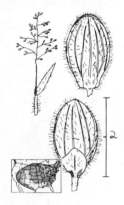

Perennial; tufted; plants 15—75 cm. tall, with open, pyramid-shaped terminal panicles blooming in May and June. Later the plants become much-branched, with loose axillary tufts of short leafy branches, interspersed with the short secondary panicles. Roadsides, old fields, open woods, meadows, swamps. Very common and widespread. *Panicum lanuginosum* is usually broken up into a number of scarcely distinguishable "species" by other authors. *P. columbianum* (see Fig. 328) is quite similar.

Figure 321

5a Plants smooth or somewhat hairy, never velvety to the touch.....6

5b Culms, leaf blades, and sheaths velvety to the touch, grayish; a smooth, sticky ring below each node. Fig. 322.
Panicum scoparium Lam.

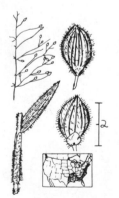

Perennial; tufted; plants 80—130 cm. tall; leaf blades large, 12—20 cm. long and 10—20 mm. wide. The terminal panicles are open, elliptical, up to 15 cm. long, produced in June and July. Later the plants become branched, with loose bunches of leaves in the axils of the sheaths of the main culm. The small secondary panicles are partially concealed among these branches. Low moist soil, mostly on the Atlantic Coastal Plain and northward in the Mississippi Valley.

Figure 322

6a Spikelets over 3 mm. long...................................7

6b Spikelets 2.7 mm. or less long................................8

7a Upper leaf sheaths bristly hairy with spreading hairs; leaf blades 6—12 mm. wide. Fig. 323.

Panicum scribnerianum Nash

Perennial; tufted; plants 20—50 cm. tall, rather stiff; sheaths sparsely covered with stiff spreading bristles or nearly smooth. The terminal panicles, produced in May and June, are 4—8 cm. long and about as broad, pyramid-shaped. After the terminal panicles have shed their spikelets, the plants become bushy-branched and produce small, simple panicles partially concealed by the tufted upper leaves. Prairies and open woods, often on dry sandy soil.

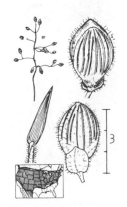

Figure 323

7b Upper sheaths glabrous or softly hairy; larger leaf blades 1.5—4 cm. wide. Fig. 324.

Panicum latifolium L.

Perennial; tufted; 45—100 cm. tall; terminal panicles produced in June, about 10 cm. long and nearly as wide, with stiff spreading branches; spikelets hairy, 3.4—3.7 mm. long. This is one of the most easily recognized of all grasses. The very broad leaf blades are heart-shaped at the base. Roadsides, woods, stream banks. The following species are also wide-leaved.

Panicum clandestinum L. has very bristly sheaths on the secondary branches. Spikelets 2.7—3 mm. long.

Panicum boscii Poir. has spikelets over 4 mm. long. The nodes of the stems are bearded with soft hairs, and the foliage is sometimes hairy.

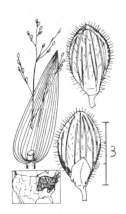

Figure 324

8a Culms glabrous 9

8b Culms covered with short fuzz and sometimes with longer hairs..10

9a Spikelets glabrous, narrowlly elliptical, 1.8—2.2 mm. long; leaf blades not hairy on the margins. Fig. 325.

Panicum dichotomum L.

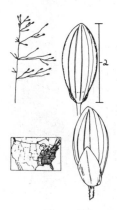

Perennial; tufted; plants erect, 30—50 cm. tall, glabrous or with a ring of hairs on the lower nodes; terminal panicles in June, 4—9 cm. long, with spreading branches. Later the culms become much-branched from the middle nodes, appearing like little trees and sometimes falling from their weight. The secondary panicles are small, with few spikelets. They extend slightly above the leaves of the branches. Widespread and common in rocky woods and on brushy land.

Panicum microcarpon Muhl. has strongly bearded nodes and tiny spikelets, 1.5—1.7 mm. long. Moist woods, meadows, and swamps.

Figure 325

9b Spikelets minutely hairy, broadly obovoid at maturity, 1.5—1.8 mm. long; leaf blades 7—14 mm. wide, with long marginal hairs at the base. Fig. 326.

Panicum sphaerocarpon Ell.

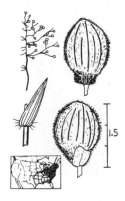

Perennial; tufted; culms 20—55 cm. long, erect or spreading; plants glabrous except for the few hairs at the base of each leaf blade, and often somewhat glaucous. Leaf blades rather broad, the top one 4—9 mm. in width. The broad panicle is less than twice as long as wide. Dry open ground and thin woods. Terminal panicles in June and July.

Panicum polyanthes Schult. has a longer, elliptical panicle, 2—4 times longer than wide, and an uppermost leaf 9—28 mm. wide. Open woods and damp ground. Southern New England to Oklahoma and southward.

Figure 326

190

10a Spikelets 2.2—2.7 mm. long; leaf sheaths glabrous; culm internodes covered with short, bent hairs. Fig. 327.

Panicum ashei **Pearson**

Perennial; tufted; plants stiffly erect, 25—50 cm. tall. The pyramid-shaped primary panicles are 5—8 cm. long and have rather few spikelets. The internodes of the culms and portions of the leaf blades tend to be purple. The plants become rather sparingly branched, with elongated branches. Dry rocky woods, brushland, often on sandy ground. Primary panicles produced from May to July.

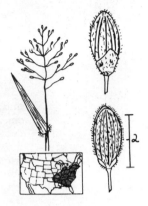

Figure 327

10b Spikelets 1.5—1.9 mm. long; leaf sheaths hairy; at least some of the sheaths and internodes covered with a mixture of long hairs and short, fine fuzz. Fig. 328.

Panicum columbianum **Scribn.**

Perennial; tufted; plant 15—50 cm. tall; leaf blades 3—6 cm. long, 3—5 mm. wide, the upper surface glabrous and the lower with fine, short hairs; primary panicles ovoid, 2—7 cm. long, produced in June and July. Later the plants become much-branched and bushy, often making mats on the ground. Dry sandy or rocky sterile ground, in the open or in thin woods.

Panicum meridionale Ashe. Plants small and delicate; leaf blades 1.5—3 cm. long, 2—4 mm. wide; upper surfaces of leaves bearing long, erect hairs; spikelets 1.3—1.5 mm. long. Sterile soil; Nova Scotia to Minnesota, south to Georgia and Alabama.

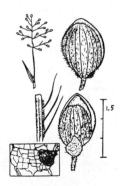

Figure 328

191

11a Spikelets glabrous or hairy, never warty....................12

11b Spikelets glabrous, covered with minute warts. Fig. 329.
                                    Panicum verrucosum Muhl.

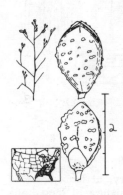

Annual; plants sprawling, the culms branch-and rooting from the lower nodes, up to 150 cm. long. The entire herbage is glabrous except for the margins of the sheaths; leaf blades thin, bright green, 5—20 cm. long, 4—10 mm. wide; ligules very short, hairy; panicles up to 30 cm. long, very open; the small (about 2 mm. long) spikelets borne in groups of 1—3 near the ends of the branches. Banks of streams; moist sandy or peaty soil. July—September.

Panicum brachyanthum Steud. has narrower leaf blades, 2—3 mm. wide; pointed spikelets 3.2—3.6 mm. long, covered with wart-based hairs. Arkansas and Oklahoma to Louisiana and Texas. August—September.

Figure 329

12a Fertile lemma minutely cross-wrinkled. Fig. 330....13

12b Fertile lemma smooth and shining.................14

Figure 330

192

13a Spikelets 5—6 mm. long, hairy. Fig. 331.
    TEXAS MILLET; COLORADO GRASS *Panicum texanum* Buckl.

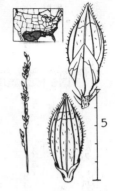

Annual; culms hairy, erect or decumbent and rooting at the lower nodes, usually 50—150 cm. long; leaves 7—16 mm. wide, 10—20 cm. long, velvety; leaf sheaths velvety; ligule hairy, about 1 mm. long; panicles narrowly cylindrical, 7—25 cm. long, up to 3 cm. in diameter; rachis and branches hairy. The lush, vigorous plants make good forage. They occur along streams and in corn and cotton fields. The common name, Colorado grass, apparently refers to the Colorado River of Texas, since this species does not occur in the state of Colorado. June—September.

Panicum arizonicum Scribn. and Merr. has similar spikelets, 3.5—3.8 mm. long; blades 6—12 mm. wide; panicle more open, with hairy branches. Western Texas to California and Mexico. August—September.

Figure 331

13b Spikelets 2—4 mm. long, glabrous. Fig. 332.
    BROWNTOP MILLET   *Panicum fasciculatum* **Swartz**

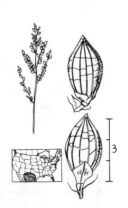

Annual; tufted, rather bushy; culms 30—100 cm. long; leaf blades 6—20 mm. wide, glabrous; ligule of hairs, 1 mm. long; sheaths glabrous or papillose-hairy; panicles 5—15 cm. long, made up of simple branches 5—10 cm. long, the spikelets nearly sessile on the branches; spikelets frequently yellowish or brown, 2—3 mm. long, with pronounced cross-veins between the longitudinal ones.

Var. *reticulatum* (Torr.) Beal has pubescent leaf blades, 6—10 mm. wide; spikelets 2.6—3.2 mm. long.

These plants are common weeds in fields, on river flats, and on waste ground. May—September.

Figure 332

14a Plants without stolons; first glume much shorter than the whole spikelet 15

14b Plants producing long, wiry stolons; spikelets very blunt, the first glume nearly as long as the spikelet. Fig. 333.
   VINE MESQUITE GRASS   *Panicum obtusum* H. B. K.

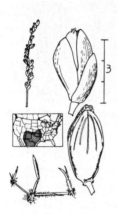

Perennial; producing elongated stolons up to 3 m. or more in length, their nodes hairy, swollen; culms erect, flattened, 20—80 cm. tall, with glabrous nodes; leaf blades 2—7 mm. wide, glabrous; ligules 1 mm. long, membranous; panicles 3—12 cm. long, very narrow, with a few ascending branches; spikelets crowded, 3—3.8 mm. long, glabrous; brownish, sterile lemma containing a palea and a staminate flower. Banks of streams, ditches, dry washes, irrigated fields. Vine mesquite furnishes some grazing, especially in the spring. It is sometimes planted for erosion control, especially on terrace outlet channels, spillways of earth dams, and flood plain flats. June—September.

Figure 333

15a Plants producing underground spikelets on root-like underground branches; aerial panicles sterile. Fig. 334. See genus 116. *Amphicarpum.*

15b Plants lacking underground spikelets; panicles fertile 16

16a Panicles with spreading or drooping branches; rhizomes present or absent........................17

Figure 334

16b Panicles long and slender, with erect branches; plants producing extensive rhizomes. Fig. 335.
MAIDEN CANE   *Panicum hemitomon* **Schult.**

Perennial; culms hard and stiff, 50—150 cm. tall; sheaths smooth or bristly; leaf blades 10—25 cm. long, 7—15 mm. wide, scabrous on top; panicles slender and spikelike, 15—30 cm. long; spikelets 2.3—2.7 mm. long. Wet ground and in water; ponds and ditches, wet fields, on the Atlantic and Gulf coastal plains. Sometimes maiden cane becomes a weed in wet fields. April—July.

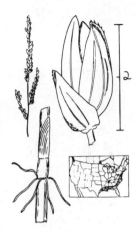

Figure 335

17a Panicle much-branched, open, the spikelets usually on long stalks, not confined to the lower sides of the branches; fertile lemma not hairy at the tip **18**

17b Panicle with mostly unbranched main branches, the spikelets on short stalks, mostly on the lower sides of the branches; fertile lemma with a tuft of minute stiff hairs at the tip **21**

18a Sheaths covered with stiff spreading hairs **19**

18b Sheaths glabrous **20**

19a Spikelets 3.5 mm. long or shorter; panicle branches slender, stiff. Fig. 336.

WITCH GRASS *Panicum capillare* L.

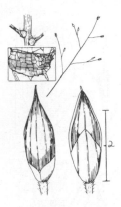

Annual; tufted; becoming bushy-branched, often 1 m. or more tall; foliage soft, leaf blades hairy on both surfaces, 5—15 mm. wide; terminal panicles large, dome-shaped, often more than half the length of the plant; numerous axillary panicles also present; bases of panicles usually hidden in the sheaths; axils of main panicle branches bearing tufts of hairs; panicles at maturity breaking away from the plant and rolling away as tumbleweeds. This is one of the commonest weedy grasses of fields and disturbed soil; widespread in the United States. About 8 similar species are found in various parts of the country, but are much less common. July—October.

Figure 336

19b Spikelets 4.5 mm. or more long; panicle branches stout, drooping. Fig. 337.

BROOMCORN MILLET; PROSO MILLET

Panicum miliaceum L.

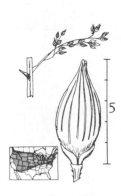

Annual; tufted; plants 20—100 cm. tall; foliage coarsely hairy or nearly smooth; leaf blades up to 30 cm. long and 20 mm. wide; panicles 10—30 cm. long, drooping, the branches scabrous; spikelets 4.5—5 mm. long, plump; fertile lemmas yellow, reddish, or brown. Proso is grown sparingly in the United States for forage, hog feed, and bird seed. The plants occur as strays on waste ground. Proso is probably native to Asia. It is cultivated in the Orient, and to a lesser extent in Europe. It is supposed to be one of the most ancient of cultivated crops, and was known to the Romans under the name of *Milium*, whence comes our word millet. July—September.

Figure 337

20a First glume rounded or broadly triangular, 1/4—1/3 as long as the spikelet; plants annual, without rhizomes. Fig. 338.

FALL PANICUM *Panicum dichotomiflorum* Michx.

Annual; tufted; plants bushy, with freely branching erect or spreading culms; often coarse, with culms up to 2 m. long in vigorous specimens; stems often zigzag, with an axillary panicle at each upper node. This is a common weed of cultivated fields, waste ground and moist soil around ponds or along streams. The size of the plants varies greatly, depending upon the moisture and fertility of the soil. July—October.

Panicum bartowense Scribn. and Merr. is similar but has bristly sheaths. Florida and the Antilles.

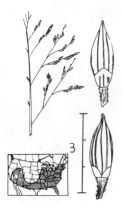

Figure 338

20b First glume at least half the length of the spikelet, tapering to a sharp point; plants perennial, with hard, rhizome-producing bases. Fig. 339.

SWITCH GRASS *Panicum virgatum* L.

Perennial; in clumps, spreading by thick scaly rhizomes; culms strong, 1—2 m. tall; panicles large and open, 15—50 cm. long; spikelets 3.5—5 mm. long, often reddish in color and at times appearing laterally compressed. Switch grass is one of the most important native grasses of the tall grass prairie, but occurs far beyond the prairie area as well. Prairies, open ground, river banks and bottomlands, thin woods. A valuable forage species, sometimes harvested as a part of wild prairie hay. July—October.

Figure 339

21a Plants producing rhizomes; spikelets scythe-shaped, set at an angle to the pedicel. Fig. 340.

Panicum anceps Michx.

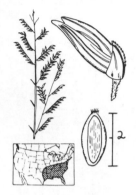

Perennial; short scaly rhizomes present; culms erect, 50—100 cm. tall; leaves smooth or hairy, elongated, 4—12 mm. wide; panicles open, 15—40 cm. long; spikelets 3.4—3.8 mm. long, curved. Open moist ground and woods, especially on sandy soil. July—September.

Panicum rhizomatum H. & C. is similar but has more elongated rhizomes, contracted panicles, and spikelets 2.4—2.8 mm. long. Sandy soil on the Atlantic and Gulf coastal plains, Maryland to Texas; Tennessee.

Figure 340

21b Plants without rhizomes; spikelets straight or nearly so, set in line with the pedicel. Fig. 341.

Panicum agrostoides Spreng.

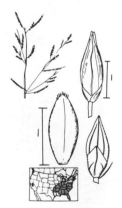

Perennial; tufted; culms 50—100 cm. tall; panicles elliptical, the branches densely clustered with nearly sessile spikelets; spikelets green or somewhat reddish, 1.8—2.2 mm. long. Moist shores and meadows, swamps, alluvial mud flats. July—September.

Panicum condensum Nash is similar but has a denser panicle; spikelets 2.2—2.5 mm. long. Wet ground on the coastal plains; Pennsylvania to Florida and Texas.

Figure 341

198

109. PASPALUM

Tufted or rhizomatous usually perennial grasses; inflorescence of 1—many 1-sided racemes, the spikelets in 2 or 4 rows along the undersides of the triangular or flattened rachis; spikelets dorsally compressed, awnless, flat on the sterile lemma side; convex on the second glume side; first glume usually absent; second glume and sterile lemma concealing the rigid fertile floret; lemma with rolled-in margins, covering the edges of the flat palea. The species occur in great numbers in warm and tropical climates. Some have forage value.

1a Plants with creeping stems; aquatic or on wet ground..........2

1b Stems not creeping...3

2a Leaf blades, sheaths, and spikelets completely glabrous; spikelets about 2 mm. long. Fig. 342.

Paspalum dissectum L.

Perennial; plants creeping by extensive stolons; erect culms 20—60 cm. tall, bearing 2—5 racemes, each 2—3 cm. long; leaf blades dark green, 3—6 cm. long, 4—5 mm. wide. The rachis of the raceme is flat and thin, 2—3 mm. wide. The first glume is lacking. Muddy flats and ditches and in shallow water. August—October.

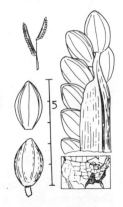

Figure 342

2b Leaf sheaths with tufts of hairs on the auricles; second glume minutely hairy; spikelets 2.5—3.5 mm. long. Fig. 343.
KNOTGRASS *Paspalum distichum* L.

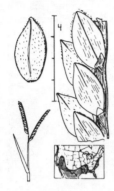

Perennial; spreading by long creeping stolons; erect culms 8—50 cm. tall; inflorescence of 2 or rarely 3 racemes, each 2—7 cm. long and somewhat curved, attached together at the summit of the culm; spikelets often with a minute first glume. Knotgrass forms large flat mats in ditches and on shores of rivers and ponds, usually in fresh water areas, rarely also in brackish localities. Found also in South America and Europe. May—September.

Figure 343

3a Inflorescences borne at the tips of the culms and in the axils of the sheaths (sometimes hidden within the sheaths)...................4

3b Inflorescences borne only at the tips of the culms, none in the leaf axils or hidden in the sheaths...................................5

4a Spikelets 1.5—1.8 mm. long, minutely hairy or glabrous. Fig. 344.
Paspalum setaceum Michx.

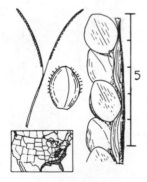

Perennial; tufted from a knotty crown; plants 30—50 cm. tall; hairy; culms slender and erect; leaf sheaths hairy; blades up to 12 cm. long and 2—6 mm. wide, hairy on both surfaces and the edges; inflorescence of 1 or 2 slender, arched racemes, 5—7 cm. long; first glume of spikelets lacking. Dry sandy soil and open woods, especially on the Atlantic and Gulf coastal plains. July—September.

Paspalum debile Michx. has spreading culms, densely grayish hairy foliage, and minutely hairy spikelets, 1.8—1.9 mm. long.

Figure 344

Most of the foliage is at the base of the plant; upper leaves short. Sandy woods of the Atlantic and Gulf coastal plains; Long Island to Mexico and Cuba.

4b Spikelets 2—2.4 mm. long. Fig. 345.

Paspalum ciliatifolium **Michx.**

Perennial; tufted; plants 40—90 cm. tall, hairy; inflorescence consisting of 1—3 racemes, each 4—17 cm. long; first glume absent. Old fields, meadows, waste ground, open woods, especially on sandy land. This is one of the commonest species, and extremely variable. There are about four closely related species found in parts of its range. June—September.

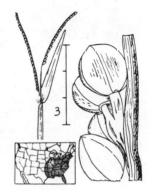

Figure 345

5a Spikelets not fringed with long hairs..........................**6**

5b Spikelets fringed with long silky hairs, borne on the edges of the second glume. Fig. 346.
DALLIS GRASS *Paspalum dilatatum* **Poir.**

Perennial; tufted; plants 50—150 cm. tall; inflorescence of 3—5 racemes, each 6—8 cm. long; first glume absent. The spikelets are more pointed than those of most other species. Dallis grass is a valuable pasture grass in the southeastern states and under irrigation in the Southwest. The spikelets may become infected by an ergot fungus and hence become poisonous to cattle. Cultivated meadows and pastures and commonly escaped to the wild. Native of South America. May— September.

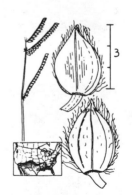

Figure 346

Paspalum urvillei Steud. (VASEY GRASS) is similar but has 12—20 racemes and strongly hispid lower sheaths. Virginia to Florida, Arkansas and Texas; California.

201

6a Plants 1—2 m. tall; spikelets 4—4.5 mm. long. Fig. 347.
Paspalum floridanum Michx.

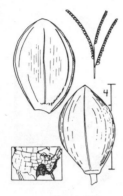

Perennial; culms single or in small tufts from short rhizomes; plants robust, 1—2 m. tall; foliage hairy or glabrous; inflorescence of 2—5 racemes each 4—12 cm. long. The axis of the racemes is strongly zigzag after the spikelets drop off. First glume absent. Low moist sandy barrens, Atlantic and Gulf coastal plains and northward in the interior. July—October.

Figure 347

6b Plants less than 1 m. tall; spikelets less than 3.5 mm. long.......7

7a Racemes 2, borne together at the end of the peduncle; stems unbranched, arising from short, woody rhizomes. Fig. 348.
BAHIA GRASS   *Paspalum notatum* Flügge

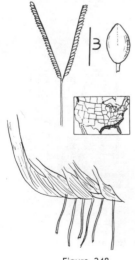

Perennial; culms stiffly erect, with 2 spreading racemes; spikelets in 2 rows along each raceme, about 3—3.5 mm. long. Bahia grass has been extensively planted for pasture and for erosion control along road shoulders in Florida and other southeastern states. It is one of the most conspicuous grasses along Florida roadsides. Introduced from tropical America. May—September.

Figure 348

7b Racemes 3 or more, borne along a central rachis; stems sprawling or erect; plants lacking rhizomes.............................8

8a Spikelets mostly in 4 rows on each raceme, over 3 mm. long; plants sprawling, often rooting at the lower nodes. Fig. 349.
Paspalum pubiflorum Rupr. ex Fourn.

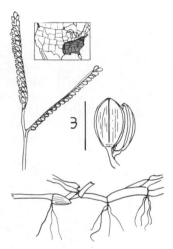

Culms up to 1 m. long, spreading; leaf sheaths often bristly; blades flat, up to 15 mm. wide; racemes 3 or more, up to 10 cm. long, rather thick because of the 4 rows of spikelets; rachis flat, up to 2 mm. wide; spikelets smooth or hairy, about 3 mm. long. Moist open ground, shrubbery, stream banks. Autumn.

Figure 349

8b Spikelets in 2 rows on each raceme, less than 3 mm. long; plants usually erect. Fig. 350.
Paspalum laeve Michx.

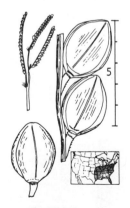

Perennial; tufted; plants 40—100 cm. tall; foliage glabrous or hairy. The inflorescence consists of 3—4 racemes, each 3—10 cm. long. The first glume is absent. This is a common species, varying greatly in hairiness of leaves and shape of spikelets. In typical plants, the spikelets are broadly oval. In var. *circulare* (Nash) Stone, they are nearly circular. Old fields, waste ground, meadow, open woods. July—October.

Figure 350

110. BRACHIARIA

Sprawling or creeping annuals or perennials; inflorescence of several 1-sided racemes, the spikelets borne in 2 rows along the lower side of a triangular or flattened rachis; first glume turned toward the rachis; sterile lemma with a palea and sometimes containing a staminate flower; fertile lemma rigid, roughened. Fig. 351.

Brachiaria platyphylla (Griseb.) **Nash**

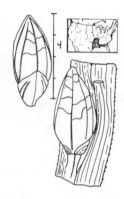

Annual; plants stooling out and sometimes rooting at the lower nodes; culms 25—40 cm. or more long; leaf blades thickish, 4—12 cm. long, 6—12 mm. wide; rachis of the racemes flattened, 1—2 mm. wide; spikelets glabrous 4—4.5 mm. long, the second glume and sterile lemma prolonged beyond the end of the fertile floret, forming a soft beak. Moist sandy ground. Formerly known as *B. extensa*. Summer.

Brachiaria ciliatissima (Buckl.) Chase has hairy foliage, and spikelets with woolly second glume and sterile lemma. It makes mats on dry sandy ground, the prostrate culms rooting at the nodes. Texas, Oklahoma, and Arkansas.

Figure 351

111. ERIOCHLOA

Inflorescence a panicle of short, 1-sided spikelike racemes; spikelets dorsally compressed, disarticulating below the glumes, with a projecting cuplike structure at the base; second glume and sterile lemma pointed, concealing the floret. Fig. 352.

PRAIRIE CUP GRASS   *Eriochloa contracta* **Hitch.**

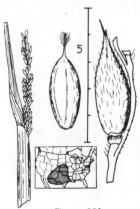

Annual; tufted, culms sometimes decumbent; plants 30—70 cm. tall. The panicles are slender, consisting of nearly erect racemes. The cuplike swelling at the base of the spikelet is a modified first glume. The fertile floret is somewhat shorter than the sterile lemma and bears a short, hairy awn which is concealed within the spikelet. Open ground, moist places, ditches. June —October.

There are seven other species of this genus, all rather similar, in the southern states.

Figure 352

112. ANTHAENANTIA

Perennials with rhizomes; inflorescence a panicle; spikelets dorsally compressed; first glume absent; second glume and sterile lemma equal, 5-nerved, covered with spreading hairs; sterile lemma with a thin, elongated membranous palea and often 3 stamens; fertile lemma and palea convex, brown, stiff, the lemma pointed. Fig. 353.

Anthaenantia rufa (Ell.) Schult.

These grasses are important native forage plants on the Atlantic and Gulf coastal plains. They have unbranched culms with very elongated, blunt-tipped lower leaves. The upper leaves have very short blades. The spikelet hairs are up to 1 mm. long and arise in dense rows between the nerves of the glume and sterile lemma. They are reddish or purplish in this species. July—November.

Anthaenantia villosa (Michx.) Beauv. is similar but the spikelets have grayish hairs. The geographic range is about the same.

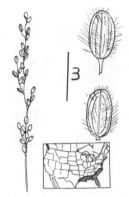

Figure 353

113. OPLISMENUS

Sprawling perennials, rooting at lower nodes; inflorescence a panicle of 1-sided racemes; spikelets dorsally compressed; first glume 3-nerved, shorter than the spikelet, with an awn 2—3 times its length; second glume 5-nerved, short-awned; sterile lemma 7-nerved, slightly longer than the glumes, blunt and awnless; fertile floret stiff, shining, awnless, the margins of the lemma covering the edges of the palea. Fig. 354.

Oplismenus setarius (Lam.) R. & S.

Stems creeping; leaf blades short, ovate; panicles on long peduncles small, made up of 3—5 racemes. Shady sites on the southern coastal plain along the Atlantic and Gulf. September—October.

Variegated leaf forms of *O. hirtellus* (L.) Beauv. are in cultivation under the name of Basket grass. The leaf blades have green, white, and purplish stripes.

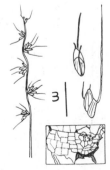

Figure 354

205

114. ECHINOCHLOA

Tufted, often rather succulent, usually annual grasses; inflorescence a panicle of 1-sided, rather crowded racemes; spikelets awned or sometimes merely pointed, dorsally compressed; first glume short; second glume and sterile lemma pointed or awned, covering the rigid, shining perfect floret; sterile lemma with a palea in its axil; edges of fertile lemma rolled in near the base only.

1a **Lower sheaths glabrous; fertile floret ovoid, 1.9—2.2 times longer than wide. Fig. 355.**

BARNYARD GRASS *Echinochloa muricata* (Beauv.) Fern.

Figure 355

Annual; tufted; plants robust, up to 1.5 m. tall, with panicles up to 20 cm. long, with spreading branches. The spikelets are covered with stout, spinelike hairs which arise from little yellowish blisters. Disturbed soil, in ditches, fields, marshes, borders of ponds. August —September.

Echinochloa crusgalli (L.) Beauv. is similar but does not have the blister-based stout spines on the spikelets. Just below the withering tip of the fertile lemma is a circle of minute hairs. These are absent in the preceding species. Fields and waste places; widespread; supposedly introduced from Europe.

1b **Lower sheaths bristly with stiff hairs; fertile floret elliptical, 2.5—3 times longer than wide. Fig. 356.**

Echinochloa walteri (Pursh) Nash

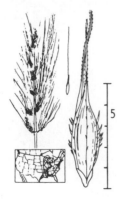

Figure 356

Annual; tufted; robust, up to 2 m. tall; panicles up to 30 cm. long. The spikelets usually bear awns 1—2.5 cm. long. Individuals with glabrous sheaths can be identified by the narrow spikelets. Wet ground or shallow water, sometimes in brackish areas, mostly on the Atlantic and Gulf coastal plains. August— September.

115. SACCIOLEPIS

Spikelets flat on the first glume side, bulged out at the base and much inflated on the second glume side; sterile lemma with a well-developed palea; fertile floret smooth and shining, dorsally compressed, much shorter than the second glume and sterile lemma. Fig. 357.

SACK GRASS *Sacciolepis striata* (L.) **Nash**

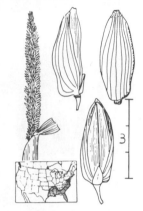

Perennial; culms often decumbent and rooting at the lower nodes, up to 2 m. long. The leaf sheaths may be bristly-hairy or smooth. Panicles dense, cylindrical, 6—30 cm. long. The spikelets are flat on the first glume side, very bulging at the base on the second glume side. Ditches, marshes and swamps, on the Atlantic and Gulf coastal plains. June—December.

Figure 357

116. AMPHICARPUM

Inflorescence a slender panicle; spikelets usually lacking a first glume; second glume and sterile lemma longer than the floret and concealing it; floret hard, smooth, boat-shaped, the edges of the lemma covering the edges of the palea; aerial spikelets usually sterile; much enlarged fruitful underground spikelets borne on the tips of slender rhizomes. Fig. 358.

PEANUT GRASS *Amphicarpum purshii* **Kunth**

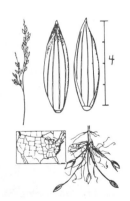

Annual; plants hairy, tufted, erect, 30—80 cm. tall. From the crown of the plant arise slender underground runners, 2—5 cm. long, each bearing a single large spikelet, 7—8 mm. long, at its tip. Most of the seed is produced by these underground spikelets, the aerial panicles being sterile. (See also Fig. 334, which shows a subterranean spikelet.) Sandy or peat soil, pine barrens of the Atlantic coastal plain. Fall.

Amphicarpum muhlenbergianum (Schult.) Hitch. is perennial, has smooth leaves and stout underground rhizomes, bearing subterranean spikelets. Pine barrens, South Carolina to Florida.

Figure 358

117. STENOTAPHRUM

Perennial; spreading by coarse stolons; leaf sheaths strongly flattened and keeled; inflorescence an erect 1-sided spike, the axis thick, elliptical in cross section, with the spikelets sunken into one side of it. Fig. 359.

ST. AUGUSTINE GRASS

Stenotaphrum secundatum (Walt.) Kuntze

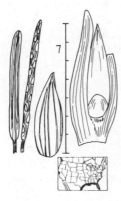

Perennial; plants spreading rapidly and extensively by stolons; erect flowering stems 10—30 cm. tall. The leaf sheaths are very much flattened and keeled; blades with rounded, blunt tips. The spikelets are similar to those of *Panicum* species, but are nearly hidden by the flanges of the rachis. The first glume and sterile lemma are exposed. This unique grass is used for lawns in some localities in the South. Occasionally plants occur with white-striped leaf blades, and these may be cultivated for ornament. June—September.

Figure 359

118. SETARIA   FOXTAIL

Panicles dense, cylindrical, bristly; spikelets interspersed with numerous long bristles (sterile branches), disarticulating just below the glumes and leaving the bristles on the rachis, except in millet, which disarticulates above the glumes; first glume short; second glume and sterile lemma nearly as long as the rigid floret.

1a Bristles upwardly-barbed or smooth; panicles not clinging to objects 2

1b Bristles downwardly-barbed, clinging to objects when the panicle is brushed upward. Fig. 360.
　　BRISTLY FOXTAIL　　　　　Setaria verticillata (L.) Beauv.

Annual; tufted; culms up to 1 m. tall. The barbed bristles of the panicles not only cause them to adhere to wool, hair, or clothing, but also to each other. After windstorms, the plants will often be densely tangled. Sometimes flies or other insects are caught in the bristles. Common in cornfields and on disturbed soil. Introduced from Europe. June—October.

Figure 360

2a Margins of sheaths bearing short hairs.........................3

2b Margins of sheaths smooth, thin and translucent; glabrous except for a few long hairs at the apex. Fig. 361.
　　YELLOW FOXTAIL　　　　　Setaria lutescens (Weigel) Hubb.

Annual; tufted; culms spreading or erect, up to 1 m. tall; panicles stiff and compact, with a pronounced golden cast imparted by the yellow bristles; back of the fertile lemma exposed, transversely corrugated. An exceedingly common weed, in cornfields or other disturbed soil. Introduced from Europe. Also known as S. glauca. July—October.

Setaria geniculata (Lam.) Beauv. has similar panicles but is a perennial, and the culms arise singly or in small tufts from knotty, much-branched rhizomes. Atlantic and Gulf coast states, from Massachusetts to Texas, lower Mississippi Valley to Illinois and Iowa.

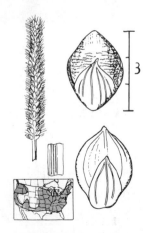

Figure 361

3a Upper surfaces of leaves glabrous.............................4

3b Upper surfaces of leaves covered with soft hairs. Fig. 362.
    NODDING FOXTAIL; GIANT FOXTAIL   *Setaria faberi* Herrm.

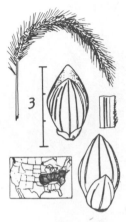

Annual; tufted; culms up to 2.5 m. tall; spikelets 2.6—2.9 mm. long. This species looks much like green foxtail, but is usually larger and has more drooping, larger panicles. The velvety leaf blades are a good mark of recognition. Although known in North America for only about 40 years, nodding foxtail is already a bad weed in parts of the eastern and middle western states. Corn, soybean, and red clover fields; gardens; disturbed soil, especially on river bottomlands. Introduced from China. July—September.

Figure 362

4a Spikelets dropping from the plants whole......................5

4b Fertile floret when ripe "shelling out" of the glumes and sterile lemma, leaving them attached to the plant. Fig. 363.
    FOXTAIL MILLET   *Setaria italica* (L.) Beauv.

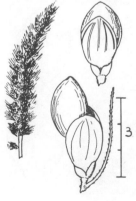

Annual; tufted; plants stout, often 1 m. or more tall, with large, often definitely lobed panicles. Foxtail millet is regarded as being closely related to the wild green foxtail. The fertile lemma is variously yellow, orange, red, brown, or blackish. Millet is cultivated to a small extent as a forage and grain crop. It is sometimes found persisting after cultivation or as a stray in the wild. Introduced from the Orient. July—October.

Figure 363

5a Plants usually 1 m. tall or shorter; leaf blades usually 1 cm. wide or narrower; plants widespread, not in coastal marshes.........6

5b Plants 1—4 m. tall; larger leaf blades 1—4 cm. wide; plants of coastal marshes along the Atlantic and Gulf of Mexico. Fig. 364.
GIANT FOXTAIL   *Setaria magna* Griseb.

Annual; tufted; culms stout and tall, up to 2 cm. thick and 4 m. tall; leaf blades flat and scabrous, up to 50 cm. long. The immense panicles reach lengths of 50 cm. and diameters of 3.5 cm. They are somewhat nodding and may be lobed at the base, thickest at the middle and tapering toward the ends. Axillary panicles are much smaller than the terminal one. Bristles 1—2 cm. long; spikelets about 2 mm. long; fertile floret smooth and shining, brown when ripe. Giant foxtail is a characteristic plant of coastal marshes, found in the interior only in Arkansas. Its range also extends to the West Indies. August—September.

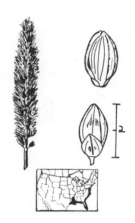

Figure 364

6a Plants annual, with soft bases and shallow roots; leaf blades usually less than 15 cm. long, flat; panicles usually less than 10 cm. long, with dense spreading bristles. Fig. 365.
GREEN FOXTAIL   *Setaria viridis* (L.) Beauv.

Annual; tufted; becoming much-branched from the base, 20—100 cm. tall; leaf sheaths glabrous except for the short cilia along the margins; blades glabrous, usually less than 10 mm. wide; panicles soft, slightly nodding near the tip; bristles green, rarely purple; spikelets 1.9—2.2 mm. long, greenish except when ripe; second glume and sterile lemma nearly covering the fertile floret; fertile lemma nearly smooth. Green foxtail is one of the commonest weeds of cornfields and other areas of disturbed soil. The bristles are sterile panicle branches. Introduced from Europe. July—October.

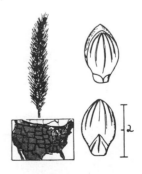

Figure 365

211

6b Plants perennial, with hard, knotty crowns; leaf blades usually folded, 15—40 cm. long; panicles slender, 2—25 cm. long, with sparse bristles. Fig. 366.

PLAINS FOXTAIL   *Setaria macrostachya* H. B. K.

Perennial; in hard tufts; culms 40—120 cm. tall; panicles slender, with the hairy rachis exposed between clusters of spikelets. The plants are leafy and are highly palatable to livestock, so that they are usually kept grazed down except in clumps of spiny bushes. Dry plains and savannas, especially along roadsides or other areas protected from grazing. April—October.

Figure 366

119. PENNISETUM

Inflorescence a dense bristly cylindrical panicle; spikelets borne in small clusters, each surrounded by a group of long bristles (sterile branches), the group of spikelets and bristles falling from the axis as a unit; spikelets dorsally compressed; first glume short; second glume and sterile lemma enclosing the stiff smooth fertile floret. Fig. 367.

FOUNTAIN GRASS   *Pennisetum setaceum* (Forsk.) Chiov.

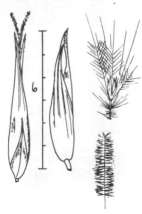

Perennial; tufted; culms up to 1 m. tall, with a hairy, pinkish or lavender, spikelike panicle. The panicle is made up of a straight central axis, 15—35 cm. long, bearing dense clusters of short branches. At maturity, each branch breaks off, carrying with it a spikelet or a small group of spikelets, surrounded by a dense tuft of long (3—4 cm.) bristles. The larger bristles may have branches, feather-fashion. This is a handsome ornamental grass, introduced from Africa. Formerly known as *P. ruppelii*. Summer.

Pennisetum glaucum (L.) R. Br. (PEARL MILLET) has a thick spike, looking like

Figure 367

that of the cat-tails. Rarely cultivated for forage in the South. Plants up to 4 m. tall. Bristles of the spikelet-groups short, barely reaching the tips of the spikelets.

120. CENCHRUS SANDBUR

Tufted weedy plants; inflorescence a spike of spiny burs, each containing 1 to several awnless spikelets; first glume short; second glume and sterile lemma mostly concealing the rigid floret; burs falling from the rachis when ripe, the spikelets remaining inside the bur and germinating there. Fig. 368.

FIELD SANDBUR *Cenchrus longispinus* **(Hack.) Fern.**

Annual; culms 20—90 cm. long, usually spreading and making mats. The spikelets are mostly concealed by the horribly spiny burs, which are made up of sterile branches. The burs are borne in short spikes along a zigzag rachis, and fall off at a touch when ripe. The spines of the burs are very sharp, and each spine is microscopically backward-ly-barbed. These spines can inflict painful and dangerous flesh wounds. Each bur contains 1 to several spikelets resembling those of species of *Panicum*. Sandbur is an undesirable weed of disturbed soil, much more common on sandy land than on heavier soils. Where it is abundant, it may furnish some feed for livestock when young. May—October.

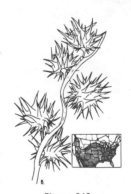

Figure 368

Cenchrus tribuloides L. (DUNE SANDBUR) has larger burs, 10—17 mm. in diameter. It grows on dunes along the Atlantic and Gulf coasts.

Cenchrus incertus Curtis is a common species in the South. It has small burs with relatively few spines that are wide and flat at the base..

213

121. TRICHACHNE

Inflorescence a panicle of 1-sided racemes; the spikelets in pairs, lanceolate, covered with long silky hairs, dorsally compressed; first glume very short, the second glume and sterile lemma covering the fertile floret, which is brown and stiffish with thin white edges covering the margins of the palea. Fig. 369.

COTTONTOP   *Trichachne californica* (Benth.) Chase

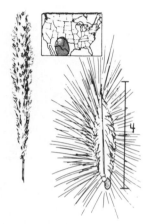

Perennial; tufted, from knotty stooling crowns; plants 30—100 cm. tall, with rather dense, slender panicles 5—10 cm. long. The panicles have a silvery white color, rarely tinged with purple when young; spikelets with a minute first glume; second glume shorter and narrower than the fertile lemma. Cottontop furnishes good summer and winter feed in the Southwest, but is grazed mostly just after rains, when it makes rapid growth. Rocky ridges, margins of fields, in brush. August—October.

Trichachne insularis (L.) Ness (SOUR-GRASS) is similar but the spikelet hairs are brownish. Florida to Arizona.

Figure 369

122. DIGITARIA   CRABGRASS

Tufted or stoloniferous annuals, rarely perennial; inflorescence of several slender 1-sided racemes; spikelets borne singly or in pairs in 2 rows on the lower side of a flattened or triangular rachis; first glume minute or absent; second glume short or equal to the sterile lemma; floret pointed, firm-textured; thin edges of the lemma covering the margins of the palea.

1a Rachis of the racemes thin and flat, with a pronounced midrib. Fig. 370.........................2

Figure 370

1b Rachis of the racemes triangular in cross section. Fig. 371.

Digitaria filiformis (L.) Koel.

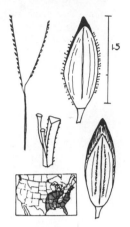

Annual; tufted; culms erect, 10—60 cm. tall; racemes 1—5, up to 10 cm. long The first glume is absent, and the equal second glume and sterile lemma nearly cover the chocolate-brown fertile floret; spikelets about 1.5 mm. long. Dry, usually sandy disturbed soil. August—October.

Figure 371

2a Fertile floret brownish-black when ripe; leaf sheaths glabrous. Fig. 372.

SMOOTH CRABGRASS *Digitaria ischaemum* (Schreb.) Muhl.

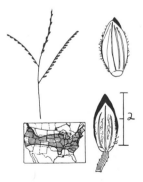

Annual; erect or spreading, often rooting at the lower nodes; culms usually 15 —40 cm. long; inflorescence usually of 2— 6 racemes. This species frequently grows with the next and is a bad weed in lawns. Disturbed soil, fields, waste places, gardens, lawns. Introduced from the Old World. August—October.

Figure 372

2b Fertile floret pale or leaden gray when ripe; leaf sheaths sparsely to densely covered with long straight hairs. Fig. 373.
     CRABGRASS   *Digitaria sanguinalis* (L.) Scop.

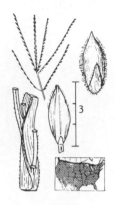

Annual; erect or spreading, usually rooting at the lower nodes; culms up to 1 m. long, the plants often forming large mounds on rich soil. Crabgrass is a serious weed in lawns. Being originally from warm climates, it starts growth when hot weather arrives. The rampant plants soon make large patches in lawns, but die out after the first frosts. They also grow abundantly in fields and waste places, sometimes furnishing some forage. Introduced from the Old World. July—October.

Figure 373

123. AXONOPUS

Creeping perennial; inflorescence of several slender 1-sided racemes; spikelets dorsally compressed; first glume absent; second glume and sterile lemma covering the stiff elliptical floret. Fig. 374.

     CARPET GRASS   *Axonopus affinis* **Chase**

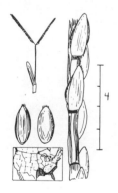

Perennial; producing extensive creeping stolons; erect culms flattened, 20—60 cm. tall; racemes 2—5 on each peduncle, 3—10 cm. long; rachis triangular in cross section, with the spikelets fitting closely against it. The first glume is absent. Low moist sandy or muck soil on the coastal plain, where it is important as a lawn and pasture grass. March—September.

Figure 374

124. LEPTOLOMA

Perennial, tufted; panicle very open, the small spikelets on the tips of stiff, elongated slender pedicels; first glume minute or absent; second glume and sterile lemma concealing the pointed fertile floret; floret stiff, brown; edges of the lemma thin, covering the margins of the palea. Fig. 375.

FALL WITCHGRASS   *Leptoloma cognatum* (Schult.) Chase

Perennial; plants stiffly spreading or erect, in large tufts; culms 30—70 cm. long; panicles very open, with stiffly spreading, thin, somewhat zigzag branches. The pedicels of the individual spikelets may be up to 20 —30 times the length of the spikelet. The second glume and sterile lemma bear appressed hairs. When mature, the panicles break off and roll away as tumbleweeds. Dry sandy open soil. May—September.

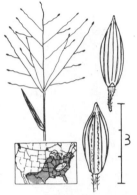

Figure 375

125. RHYNCHELYTRUM

Panicles rosy-purple, turning gray; spikelets laterally compressed, concealed by the abundant hairs, disarticulating below the glumes; first glume minute, concealed by the hairs; second glume and sterile lemma equal, very hairy; fertile floret stiff, boat-shaped, acute. Fig. 376.

NATAL GRASS; RUBY GRASS
Rhynchelytrum repens (Willd.) Hubb.

Perennial; tufted; plants about 1 m. tall; panicles rosy-purple, 10—15 cm. long; spikelets on bent or curled pedicels, and densely covered with purple hairs. The second glume and sterile lemma have short awns that are concealed by the hairs. The lateral compression of the spikelets is very atypical for the Panicoideae. Dry sandy land and open woods. Natal grass, an introduction from Africa, is grown in Florida for forage and has become naturalized there and also along the Gulf Coast. Formerly known as *Tricholaena rosea*. Winter.

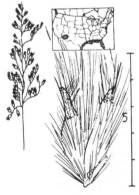

Figure 376

Tribe 26. Andropogoneae

126. IMPERATA

Rhizomatous perennials; inflorescence spikelike, made up of racemes bearing pairs of equal, awnless, unequally-stalked spikelets, which disarticulate from the tips of the pedicels; glumes equal, concealing the shorter delicate sterile and fertile florets. Fig. 377.

SATINTAIL   *Imperata brevifolia* **Vasey**

Perennial; culms arising from hard scaly rhizomes; culms 1—1.5 m. tall, with elongated leaves and slender, silvery-hairy panicles, 15—35 cm. long and 1—3 cm. thick. The spikelets are about 3 mm. long and have a ring of long white hairs at the base, with some hairs also attached to the backs of the glumes. The spikelets fall from the rachis when ripe. Deserts. July—September.

Imperata cylindrica (L.) Beauv. (COGON GRASS) has been introduced in western Florida. Spikelets 4—5 mm. long. This species has forage uses but may become a weed, because of its extensive rhizomes.

Figure 377

127. ERIANTHUS

Tall perennial grasses; inflorescence plumy, of rames; rachis disarticulating, separating the spikelet pairs; spikelets of each pair equal, 1 sessile and the other stalked, with a tuft of long hairs attached to the callus; spikelets dorsally compressed, with long stiff glumes concealing the delicate sterile and fertile florets; awns usually present. Fig. 378.

SILVER PLUMEGRASS *Erianthus alopecuroides* **(L.) Ell.**

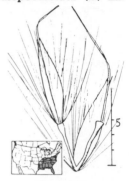

Perennial; culms strong and tall, 1—3 m. long, arising from short, scaly rhizomes. The nodes, upper portions of the sheaths, and peduncles are appressed-hairy. The dense silky-hairy elliptical panicles are 20—30 cm. long. Each yellowish spikelet bears a tuft of long silvery or purplish hairs from the base, as well as a few hairs on the upper portions of the glumes. Spikelets 5—6 mm. long, with a flattened and twisted awn 1—1.5 cm. long. The rachis breaks up into individual joints when ripe. Open woods, wet low ground, hammocks. September—October.

Figure 378

Erianthus contortus Ell. is similar, but has dark brown glumes.

Erianthus giganteus (Walt.) Muhl. (*E. saccharoides*) is similar but has straight, untwisted awns which are not flattened in cross section.

Erianthus ravennae (L.) Beauv. (RAVENNA GRASS) is a cultivated perennial, with culms up to 4 m. tall and large silky grayish plumes; it is hardy in the southern two thirds of the United States. Awns very short or absent. Native to Europe. Fall.

128. MISCANTHUS

Tall perennials; inflorescence fan-shaped, of numerous long, silky racemes; spikelets paired, identical but on unequal stalks, dorsally compressed; glumes equal, concealing the delicate sterile and fertile florets; a tuft of silky hairs borne at the base of each spikelet and partly concealing it; disarticulation below each spikelet. Fig. 379.

EULALIA *Miscanthus sinensis* **Anderss.**

Perennial, forming large clumps; culms 2—3 m. tall, with plumelike, silvery-gray, fan-shaped panicles of long, hairy racemes. The spikelets are about 5 mm. long, with a ring of hairs about as long as the spikelet, attached at the base of the glumes. The spikelets fall from the rachis when ripe. Cultivated widely as an ornamental, and occasionally escaping to the wild around inhabited places. Horticultural forms with white-striped or cross-banded leaves are also grown. Native to Asia. September—October.

Miscanthus sacchariflorus (Maxim.) Hack., which has pure white panicles of awnless spikelets and spreads by vigorous rhizomes,

Figure 379

has become a weed in the North Central States and is cultivated for ornament. August—November.

129. SACCHARUM

Giant tropical grasses with large, plumy panicles; inflorescence made up of rames; spikelets paired, awned, equal, 1 sessile and the other on a pedicel; rachis breaking up into individual joints when mature, each bearing a pair of spikelets; glumes equal, concealing the thin, delicate fertile and sterile florets. Fig. 380.

SUGAR CANE   *Saccharum officinarum* L.

Figure 380

Perennial; tall stout plants, with culms 3—5 m. tall and up to 3 cm. thick. The stiff, elongated leaves have scabrous cutting edges. Panicles large and plumelike, 20—60 cm. long. Sugar cane is widely cultivated in the tropics for the production of sugar, but in the United States is grown only in the southern end of the Mississippi Valley and in Florida. The plants seldom bloom.

Erianthus ravennae (L.) Beauv. (RAVENNA GRASS) has a large, plumelike panicle, up to 60 cm. long, and slender culms up to 4 m. tall. Cultivated for ornament and hardy in the southern two-thirds of the country.

130. ANDROPOGON   BLUESTEM

Perennials; tufted or with rhizomes; inflorescence of 1 or more rames; spikelets in pairs of 1 sessile, perfect-flowered, awned spikelet and 1 small, stalked, sterile or rarely staminate spikelet; the rachis when mature disarticulating into individual internodes, each with a pair of spikelets attached; spikelets dorsally compressed; glumes long, stiff, concealing the delicate sterile and fertile florets.

1a **Rames several to many on each peduncle**......................2
1b **Rames 1 on each peduncle. Fig. 381.**

LITTLE BLUESTEM   *Andropogon scoparius* Michx.

Figure 381

Perennial; tufted; plants green or reddish, 50—150 cm. tall; foliage smooth or hairy. The rames are borne on slender peduncles from the axils of the sheaths and the tips of the culms. The rachis joints and pedicels are strongly hairy. Little bluestem is characteristically a plant of dry prairies and plains, but occurs to some extent over nearly the entire United States. Prairies, old fields, rocky slopes and open woods. Little bluestem furnishes much grazing in the Middle West and West, especially for cattle and horses. August —October.

Nine other species, similar in having only 1 raceme on each peduncle, occur in the southern United States, but are much rarer.

2a Stalked spikelet sterile, reduced to a small rudiment or nearly absent; rames feathery, white....................................3

2b Stalked spikelet staminate, similar to the sessile one but awnless; rames green or purplish in color, not feathery with fine hairs. Fig. 382.
BIG BLUESTEM   *Andropogon gerardii* Vitman

Perennial; tufted or with short rhizomes; plants green or reddish, 1—2 m. tall or even taller; foliage sometimes hairy. The plants bear 3—6 reddish rames at the tip of the culm, and usually some smaller inflorescences from the axils of the leaves. Big bluestem was one of the principal grasses of the tall grass prairie which produced the rich soils of our corn belt. Very little of such grassland still exists, but this species is still very common on untilled land in the prairie area. Farther east it is less common, but occurs on steep slopes, in meadows, and along river banks. This is an important forage species, and still provides much wild hay from native prairie. Also known as *A. furcatus* and *A. provincialis.* August—October.

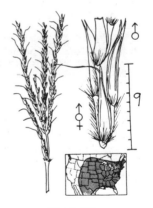

Figure 382

Andropogon hallii Hack. (SAND BLUESTEM) has more elongated rhizomes and yellowish spikelets. Sandhills of the Great Plains and Rocky Mountain area.

3a Inflorescence of 2—4 rames, which are enclosed at their bases by a leaf sheath. Fig. 383.

BROOMSEDGE   *Andropogon virginicus* L.

Perennial; tufted; 50—100 cm. tall; foliage smooth or somewhat hairy, often reddish; culms bearing feathery-hairy inflorescences at the tip and from the axils of the leaves of the upper half of the culm. Broomsedge is a plant of sterile open hillsides, abandoned fields, and thin woods. It usually indicates poor soil. The forage value is apparently low, especially when the plants are mature. August—October.

About 14 other similar species or varieties occur in the southeastern states, mostly on the Coastal Plain. Most striking of these is the following:

Figure 383

Andropogon glomeratus (Walt.) B. S. P. (*A. virginicus*, var. *abbreviatus* (Hack.) Fern.). All the inflorescences are condensed into a dense, broomlike cluster at the top of the stem. Southeastern states; Texas to California, often on damp, low ground.

3b Inflorescence a terminal panicle of numerous rames; leafy bracts absent from the panicle. Fig. 384.

SILVER BEARDGRASS   *Andropogon saccharoides* Sw.

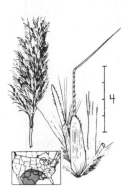

Perennial; tufted; rather bushy; culms 60—130 cm. tall; foliage usually glabrous, becoming reddish when mature. The long-stalked panicles are silvery-white, oblong, 7—15 cm. long. The rachis joints and pedicels are fringed with long white hairs. Sessile spikelet of each pair about 4 mm. long, the pedicellate one rudimentary. Silver beardgrass and several of its close relatives are valuable forage grasses in parts of the Southwest, but are easily exterminated by overgrazing. Prairies and plains, rocky slopes, draws and dry washes, often on sandy soil. June—September.

Figure 384

Andropogon barbinodis Lag. is taller, with a short, fan-shaped panicle, with spikelets 5—6 mm. long. The nodes of the culms are prominently bearded. Oklahoma to California and Mexico.

131. ELYONURUS

Inflorescence an erect cylindrical rame, disarticulating into individual internodes, each bearing an awnless, nearly sessile spikelet and a stalked, staminate spikelet on a thick pedicel; spikelets dorsally compressed; first glume bearing 2 flanges on the back side which grasp the edges of the second glume; second glume slightly keeled, thinner than the first. Fig. 385.

Elyonurus tripsacoides H. & B. ex Willd.

Erect plants, forming large clumps; perennial, with short rhizomes; culms 1 m. or more tall, branching; rachis joints short and thick, disarticulating very obliquely; the staminate spikelet and its thick pedicel fitting closely against the "sessile" perfect-flowered spikelet. Ditches, roadsides, low ground, Gulf States and Mexico. June—September.

Elyonurus barbiculmis Hack. is similar, but the spikelets are very woolly. Western Texas to Arizona.

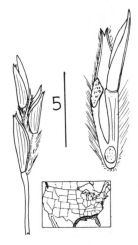

Figure 385

132. MICROSTEGIUM

Inflorescence of several rames; rachis internodes flat, widened toward the upper end; disarticulation at the base of each internode, which falls carrying at its base 1 stalked and 1 sessile spikelet, the 2 alike in size, both perfect-flowered, laterally compressed, and awnless. Fig. 386.

Microstegium vimineum (Trin.) Camus

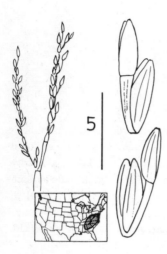

The plants are straggling annuals, rooting at the lower nodes. The glumes are papery in texture. The inner bracts of the spikelet (sterile and fertile lemma) are extremely small or missing altogether. If present, they are thin nerveless scales. Sometimes the fertile lemma bears an awn. Moist shady banks, southeastern United States. October.

Figure 386

133. ARTHRAXON

Inflorescence a small, fan-shaped group of slender spikes; rachis disarticulating into individual internodes, each bearing a single spikelet at its base; spikelets lanceolate, pointed, laterally compressed; glumes equal, scabrous, greenish and papery. Fig. 387.

Arthraxon hispidus (Thunb.) Makino

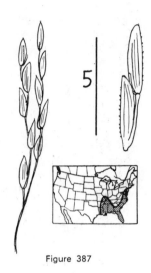

Low creeping annual with bristly sheaths and short broad blades with cordate bases. At the base of many spikelets a minute bristle is borne, representing the stalked spikelet usually found in this tribe. The inner parts of the spikelet are very delicate and membranous. The fertile lemma bears a minute awn, usually hidden inside the glumes. Low meadows, riverbanks; southern Pennsylvania to Florida, Louisiana, and Missouri. Introduced from the Orient. September—October.

Figure 387

134. SORGHUM

Tall annuals or perennials; inflorescence a branched panicle of short rames consisting of 2—7 pairs of spikelets, all but the terminal segments bearing a hard, sessile, awned perfect-flowered spikelet and a stalked, awnless, soft-textured staminate one; terminal segment with 2 staminate spikelets.

1a **Spikelets when ripe disarticulating from the tip of the pedicel; end of pedicel cup-shaped; rhizomes present; weed. Fig. 388.**
   JOHNSON GRASS *Sorghum halepense* **(L.) Pers.**

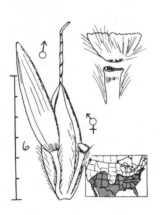

Figure 388

Perennial; culms tall and stout, 0.5—2 m. tall, arising from thick, wide-spreading rhizomes; panicle open, pyramid-shaped, 15—50 cm. long. The sessile spikelet is perfect and fertile, hard, and rather plump, about 5 mm. long. The awn falls off readily, so the spikelets are often awnless. The pedicellate spikelets are of softer texture, staminate, narrower, and awnless. The sessile spikelet at the end of each short rame is accompanied by 2 pedicellate spikelets. The fertile spikelets vary from straw-colored to almost black. This species, regarded as a noxious weed in the southern states, is very similar to the annual crop, Sudan grass. Despite its bad traits, Johnson grass furnishes a great deal of forage and is readily eaten by livestock. Eurasian.

1b Spikelets when ripe breaking from the plant with the upper end of the pedicel, leaving a jagged stub; rhizomes lacking; crop plant. Fig. 389.

SUDAN GRASS *Sorghum sudanense* (Piper) Stapf

Annual; tufted; culms 1—3 m. tall. The plants resemble those of Johnson grass but lack the rhizomes. Widely cultivated for annual pasture and hay and sometimes found as a stray from dropped seed. Native to North Africa.

Sorghum bicolor (L.) Moench. (SORGHUM) this species includes a large group of rather cornlike plants, cultivated in warm sections of the country for grain, fodder, silage, and syrup. The leaves and stems greatly resemble Indian corn, but the spikelets, similar to those of Johnson grass, are all borne in panicles at the tips of the stems. The grains may be black, brown, reddish, gray, or white. In many varieties, the grain becomes large enough to burst out of the glumes. Milo, hegari, feterita, durra, kafir corn, shallu, amber cane, broomcorn are all varieties of this species. Broomcorn is not used for forage, but the stiff, elongated panicle branches are the broomstraw of commerce.

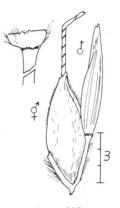

Figure 389

135. SORGHASTRUM

Tall perennials; inflorescence a much-branched panicle of stalked short rames, each consisting of a few rachis segments; each segment bearing a sessile, hard, dorsally-compressed, awned, perfect-flowered spikelet and a hairy sterile pedicel. The "stalked spikelet" is completely absent. The terminal segment of each rame bears 2 pedicels. Fig. 390.

INDIAN GRASS   *Sorghastrum nutans* (L.) **Nash**

Figure 390

Perennial; in tufts from short rhizomes; plants 1—2.5 m. tall; foliage usually smooth. Panicles narrow and rather dense, 15—30 cm. long. The panicle has a "gold-and-silver" aspect because of the yellow, 5—6 mm. long spikelets and the copious white hairs which fringe the rachises and pedicels. The prominent anthers are golden yellow. The panicle is made up of short rames of 1—3 joints. Each sessile spikelet is accompanied by a hairy pedicel. The rames break up into individual joints at maturity, each bearing a spikelet and a rachis joint and pedicel. Indian grass is one of the principal grasses of the tall grass prairie. It is also found in the eastern states and the Rocky Mountains. It forms an important component of wild prairie hay. Prairies, plains, stream banks, dry hills. July—September.

136. MANISURIS

Perennials; tufted; inflorescence a single stiff cylindrical rame, disarticulating when mature into individual internodes, each of which bears an awnless, sessile, perfect-flowered spikelet and a thick-stalked rudimentary one attached to the thickened rachis joint, fitting closely together and forming a smooth cylindrical structure.

1a First glume with transverse corrugations. Fig. 391.

Manisuris rugosa (Nutt.) Kuntze

Perennial; culms from hard, knotty crowns; culms flattened, much-branched, 70—120 cm. tall, with numerous axillary rames. Rames slender, "rat-tail"-like, brownish, 4—8 cm. long, tapering from the middle toward the base and apex. They break up into individual joints readily, each joint bearing a perfect sessile spikelet and a sterile spikelet on a thickened pedicel. The first glume of the spikelet is strongly corrugated across the width. Wet pine woods and bogs, Atlantic and Gulf coastal plains. September.

Other similar species are found in the southern states, differing in the degree of roughness, pitting, etc. of the first glume.

Figure 391

1b First glume smooth or pitted, not corrugated. Fig. 392.

Manisuris cylindrica (Michx.) Kuntze

Culms erect, up to 1 m. tall; inflorescences at the tip of the culm and in leaf axils, slender and curved, up to 15 cm. long; spikelets 4—5 mm. long, first glume pitted along the nerves. Pine woods and roadsides, Atlantic and Gulf coastal plains, northward to Missouri. September—October.

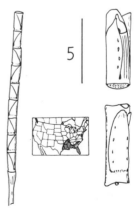

Figure 392

137. HACKELOCHLOA

Tufted, much-branched annual with terminal and axillary rames; spikelets paired, the sessile spikelet spherical, with a rough pitted blackish surface; rachis joint and pedicel united; stalked spikelet flat, staminate. Fig. 393.

Hackelochloa granularis (L.) Kuntze

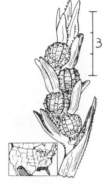

Annual; tufted; culms 30—100 cm. tall, much-branched. The culms have numerous axillary rames; sheaths and culms covered with hairs which arise from little blisters. The individual spikelets are 1—2 mm. long. The rames break up into individual joints, each bearing a sessile perfect spikelet which is blackish, and a strongly laterally compressed and winged staminate spikelet, which is green or reddish in color. This unusual grass is a native of the Old World tropics, but has been introduced into our southern states. It may yield some forage. Fall.

Figure 393

138. EREMOCHLOA

Perennial, with many leafy stolons; inflorescence a single erect rame, elliptical in cross section, the overlapping spikelets all on one side; sessile spikelet dorsally compressed, the first glume with a membranous fringe at the apex, notched at the center; pedicellate spikelet minute, abortive, on a broad leathery pedicel. Fig. 394.

CENTIPEDE GRASS   *Eremochloa ophiuroides* (Munro) Hack.

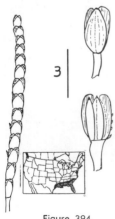

Centipede grass is raised in the southeastern states as a lawn grass. It makes a thick lush turf by the interweaving of many stiff stolons. The little purplish flowering spikes are usually 10—15 cm. tall. The axis is rather wiry and does not seem to disarticulate. The sessile spikelets have a broad leathery first glume, with short bristles along the edges. Introduced from southeastern Asia. Summer.

Figure 394

139. HETEROPOGON

Inflorescence a single rame on a long peduncle; rachis when mature mostly disarticulating into single internodes, each with a sharp hairy point, bearing a pair of unlike spikelets. Fig. 395.

TANGLEHEAD   *Heteropogon contortus* (L.) Beauv.

Perennial; tufted; plants 20—80 cm. tall; leaf sheaths flattened and keeled; rames borne at the tips of slender peduncles. The pairs of spikelets at the base of each rame are all staminate. In the upper portion of the rame, each pair consists of a sessile perfect spikelet and a stalked staminate spikelet. The sessile spikelet has a long, bent awn and a hairy rachis joint, which is attached below the base of the glumes. This spikelet greatly resembles the floret of some species of *Stipa*. Attached at the base of the perfect spikelet is a short pedicel bearing an awnless, laterally-compressed and winged staminate spikelet. The two spikelets of each pair fall as a unit.

Figure 395

Because of the sharp hairy callus and stiff awn, the perfect spikelets may injure grazing sheep. A good forage grass when not in fruit. Rocky deserts in the Southwest; found throughout the tropics of both Old and New World. June—September.

Heteropogon melanocarpus (Ell.) Benth. has staminate spikelets with glabrous glumes, a row of glandular spots running down the middle of the glume. Southeastern states and Arizona.

140. TRACHYPOGON

Inflorescence a single erect rame, its rachis not disarticulating; spikelet pairs consisting of a stalked, awned, perfect-flowered spikelet and a sessile, awnless staminate spikelet. Fig. 396.

CRINKLE AWN   *Trachypogon secundus* (Presl) Scribn.

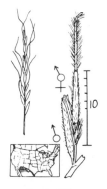

Perennial; tufted; 60—120 cm. tall; herbage nearly smooth but the nodes bearing a circle of stiff, erect hairs. The erect slender rame is 10—20 cm. long. The rachis remains whole with the short-pedicellate or sessile staminate spikelets attached to it. The longer-pedicellate perfect spikelets break from the rachis with their hairy, rigid pedicels attached. The perfect spikelet looks very much like the floret of some species of *Stipa*. The lemma is 6—8 mm. long, with a bent and twisted awn 3—6 cm. long. Rocky dry hills. May—October.

Figure 396

141. COIX

Cornlike annuals; pistillate spikelets borne in hard, bony beads, each borne on the apex of an axillary peduncle; staminate inflorescence of a few spikelets, borne on a stalk which emerges through the orifice of the bead. Fig. 397.

JOB'S TEARS *Coix lacryma-jobi* L.

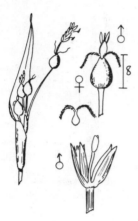

Figure 397

Plants coarse, up to 2 m. tall, abundantly branching from the upper nodes. Each peduncle bears a hard, shiny, white, grayish, or black bead, from the upper end of which protrudes a short inflorescence consisting of a few joints bearing sessile and pedicellate staminate or sterile spikelets, in somewhat irregular combinations. Staminate spikelets consist of 2 glumes, enclosing 2 staminate florets. Within the bead is borne a single pistillate spikelet and 2 slender, tubular, sterile spikelets, along with the stalk of the staminate inflorescence. The stigmas protrude from the mouth of the bead. The staminate inflorescence breaks away and the beads fall from the plant when ripe. Job's tears is cultivated as a curiosity, and for the "beads," which are used in rosaries and jewelry. The plants may be found in the wild in the southern states. Introduced from the tropics of the Old World. Late summer.

142. TRIPSACUM

Peduncles at the tips of the culms and from the axils of the upper leaves, each bearing 1—several stiff spikes; spikelets unisexual; the bony lower segment of each spike bearing only pistillate spikelets, the thinner upper portion only paired staminate ones. Fig. 398.

GAMA GRASS   *Tripsacum dactyloides* L.

Perennial; in large clumps, from thick rhizomes. The plants reach 2—3 m. in height. The spikes are borne singly or 2—3 together at the tips of long leafless peduncles. The basal portion of each spike consists of a series of hardened, smooth, hollowed-out joints, each nearly enclosing a single pistillate spikelet. These joints break apart readily when ripe. The upper portion of each spike is made up of a series of joints, each bearing 2 sessile staminate spikelets. This portion of the spike is shed whole when the pistillate rachis breaks up. Gama grass is a close relative of corn and has been experimentally crossed with it. The plants are leafy and may produce some forage, but they are seldom abundant. River banks and moist ground. June—October.

Figure 398

143. EUCHLAENA

Plants large and cornlike; annual; much-branched; staminate spikelets in a terminal tassel; pistillate spikelets in short, bony spikes, surrounded by husks and borne in the leaf axils. Fig. 399.

TEOSINTE *Euchlaena mexicana* **Schrad.**

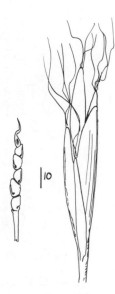

Teosinte is a tropical American grass, sometimes cultivated for forage or as a curiosity in the United States. The odd pistillate inflorescences consist of a single row of hard, bony rachis joints. The single styles, resembling the "silks" of corn, protrude from the tips of the husks. Usually a number of these spikes are borne in the axil of a single upper leaf. A single pistillate spikelet is sunken into each rachis joint. The joints separate freely when ripe. The soft staminate spikelets have 2 long glumes and 2 florets. They are paired along the rames of the tassel.

Teosinte is closely related to corn and can be experimentally crossed with it. Some authors place it in the genus *Zea*, but the plants are readily distinguished by the pistillate spike.

Figure 399

144. ZEA

Tall cultivated annual; staminate spikelets soft, paired, in a large tassel at the tip of the stem; pistillate spikelets borne in longitudinal rows on a thick axillary cob which is enclosed by leafy husks. Fig. 400.

MAIZE; INDIAN CORN   *Zea mays* L.

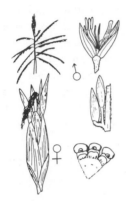

Tufted; plants exceedingly variable in size and habit, but characteristically with thick, solid stalks. The pistillate inflorescence (ear) has paired rows of spikelets. The glumes, sterile and fertile lemmas form the "chaff" that remains on the cob. In a few varieties, such as Country Gentleman, both florets of each pistillate spikelet develop grains, producing very crowded and irregular rows.

Figure 400

Corn is unusual in having united styles, which form the "silk." The staminate inflorescence (tassel), is much-branched and bears pairs of spikelets, one of each pair being sessile and the other pedicellate. Because of the great crowding of the staminate spikelets, the arrangement may be obscured. The staminate spikelets are each 2-flowered.

Corn never persists after cultivation and is unknown in the wild state. It is thought that it originated in Central America.

Figure 401

INDEX AND PICTURED-GLOSSARY

APEX: the tip of a leaf, 4. Fig. 402

Figure 402

Auricle 4
AURICLES: small pointed or rounded projections at the base of the blade, 4. Fig. 403

Figure 403

AWN: a protruding midrib of a glume or lemma, forming a beard or bristle. Lateral nerves rarely produce awns, 6. Fig. 404

Figure 404

B

BLADE: the elongated spreading portion of a grass leaf, 4. Fig. 405

Figure 405

INDEX

Figure 406

C

Figure 407

D

Figure 408

INDEX

Figure 409

E

F

Figure 410

G

Figure 411

INDEX

L

Figure 412

Figure 413

Figure 414

M

N

NERVE: one of the vascular bundles of a leaf or other plant structure, also called a vein, 4, 6
NODE: the usually swollen joint of a stem, at which a leaf is attached, 3. Fig. 415

Figure 415

O

OVARY: the swollen lower portion of the pistil, which contains the seed. Fig. 416

Figure 416

Ovary 5

P

PALEA: the inner of the two bracts which enclose a grass flower, 5, 6. Fig. 417

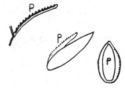

Figure 417

PANICLE: a much-branched inflorescence, bearing spikelets on pedicels, 4
PEDICEL: the stalk of a single spikelet, 5. Fig. 418

Figure 418

PEDUNCLE: the stalk of an inflorescence, 5
PETIOLE: a leaf stalk (absent in most grasses except bamboos).

Figure 419

Q

R

Figure 420

Figure 421

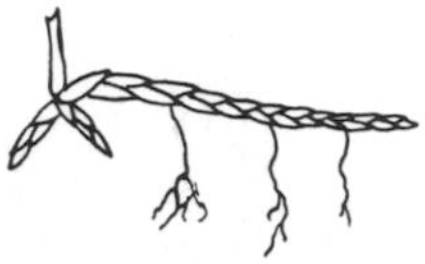

Figure 422

S

INDEX

INDEX